Flight of the
FALCON

Flight of the
FALCON

MICHAEL TENNESEN

KEY PORTER BOOKS

Canadian Cataloguing in Publication Data
Tennesen, Michael, 1944-
   Flight of the falcon

Includes index.
ISBN 1-55013-285-7

1. Falcons.   2. Peregrine falcon.   3. Falconry –
History.   I. Title.

QL696.F34T4 1992   598.9'18   C91-095315-5

Decorative archival drawings on the following pages are courtesy of the Royal Ontario Museum: peregrine, p.7; hobby, p.23; orange-legged hobby, p.43; kestrel, p.63; goshawk, p.81; merlin, p.101.

Design: *Scott Richardson*
Illustrations and map: *Dorothy Siemens*
Typesetting: *MacTrix DTP*
Printed and bound in Hong Kong
by BookArt Inc., Toronto.

Key Porter Books Limited
70 The Esplanade
Toronto, Ontario
Canada M5E 1R2

Distributed in the United States of America by:
Publishers Group West
4065 Hollis
Emeryville, CA 94608

92 93 94 95 96 5 4 3 2 1

Pages ii/iii:
Only in the Middle East is falconry still practiced with any of the fanfare that it was accorded during the Middle Ages. (Photo by Hans Christian Heap/ Planet Earth Pictures)

Page iv:
The Old World kestrel is called the "windhover" because it attacks its prey from its perch or while hovering in the wind. (Photo by Nico Myburgh)

Opposite:
The gyrfalcon, the largest of all falcon species, preys on ptarmigan, ground squirrels, and Arctic hares. (Photo by Fred Bruemmer)

CONTENTS

Preface *1*

1. Sky Hunter *7*

2. The Sport of Kings *23*

3. The Season of Awakening *43*

4. The Long Journey *63*

5. The Poisoned Egg *81*

6. Driven Out of House and Home *101*

Falcon Species *119*

Birds of Prey Organizations and Research Groups *134*

Index *135*

PREFACE

Each fall Stephen Hoffman, founding president of HawkWatch International (shown here with a peregrine falcon), and colleagues occupy a station at the crest of the Goshutes to study raptors.

Peregrine falcons migrate along the Goshutes, some traveling all the way from Alaska to Argentina.

IT WAS STEPHEN HOFFMAN, FOUNDING PRESIDENT OF HAWKWATCH International, in Albuquerque, New Mexico, who sparked my interest in falcons. I met him on a cold October day in 1983. The first snows had dusted the mountaintops in northeastern Nevada, and I'd just climbed through the pine trees to the 10,000-foot-high (3000-m) crest of the Goshute Mountain Range, where Hoffman and a number of biologists were gathered.

The Goshutes, a 70-mile-long (110-km) ridge bordering the barren salt flats of the Great Salt Lake Desert in the western United States, is a frequented migration route for birds of prey traveling from Canada and Alaska to Latin America. Each year Hoffman and his colleagues occupy a station at the crest of the mountain to study the birds.

I had written on environmental subjects since the early 1970s, but covered mostly mammals. Though I had seen falcons, hawks, and eagles near my home in southern California, I had yet to actively study them. Stephen Hoffman and the Goshutes changed all that.

When I reached the top, I dropped my pack and sought out Hoffman, who was manning the trapping station. As I approached, he was rushing about madly: hurriedly fixing a net in front of the blind, racing back to the shelter where I waited, then pushing me back inside the shelter.

"Hurry up, get in there" was our introduction. From inside what looked like a World War II bomb shelter, we peered out at a winged speck approaching along the crest of the ridge. About 25 feet (8 m) in front of us, a lure bird was positioned in the center of a maze of invisible mist nets. The speck, a raptor, seemed to be closing in on it.

About a quarter of a mile out, the raptor folded back its wings and went into a dive. My inexperienced eyes lost sight of the bird until the last moment when, closing in for the kill, its wings unfolded like a parachute, its talons stretched forward, the bird slammed into the net.

Hoffman flew out of the blind and rushed to untangle his catch. "It's a falcon — a merlin!" he yelled.

The bird was blue-gray, almost slate, with a whitish throat and dark patterns on its face and tail. It held its head high, its dark eyes staring back at us most menacingly, looking rather regal even while it endured the demeaning banding of its leg, the drawing of its blood, and the clipping of the tip of one of its feathers before being released to return to its migratory journey.

On the Goshutes I saw a number of regal birds of prey, even a golden eagle, diving into those nets, though the dive of the merlin was the most memorable. I became more interested in the falcons when Hoffman told me their dive was the fastest of all birds of prey, up to 200 miles an hour (320 km/h) for some of the larger species.

Since that visit I have traveled to Point Reyes Seashore in northern California and to the Grand Canyon in Arizona to see falcons. I have visited the nesting grounds of the prairie falcon in the Snake River in Idaho, and watched the peregrines flying in from Greenland at Padre Island off Texas. And I have watched the bat falcons in the jungles of Tikal in Guatemala.

Falcons, like humans, live at the top of the food chain, where they are sensitive to the poisons we use and the habitat we destroy. By studying falcons we learn not only what we are doing to them but what we may be doing to ourselves. And by protecting falcons we are also protecting the prey species and habitat. As we watch the peregrine falcon return from a close call with extinction, we can be satisfied that we have done something good not just for this bird but for ourselves as well.

I am extremely grateful to a number of people who contributed to this book. Morley Nelson, falcon biologist, cinematographer, and patron saint of the Snake River Birds of Prey Area in Idaho, taught me the language of the falcons. Brian Walton, at the Predatory Bird Research Group in Santa Cruz, California, allowed me to view his fine breeding stock of falcons and pointed the way to Point Reyes. Bill Burnham, Cal Sandfort, Bill Heinrich, Rick Watson, and Willard

GEORGE HUEY

The Goshute Mountain Range, a ridge bordering the Great Salt Lake Desert in the western United States, is a frequented route for hawks, eagles, and falcons that migrate from Canada and Alaska to Latin America.

Heck, with the World Center for Birds of Prey in Idaho, all shared with me their vast knowledge of falcons.

Wayne Nelson, a biologist with the Alberta Fish and Wildlife Division, contributed the excitement behind his scientific observations of the falcons on the Queen Charlotte Islands, and Hartmut Walter shared with me his classic experiences with Eleonora's falcons in Madagascar and the Mediterranean.

Tom Maechtle and Scott Francis, my Padre Island hosts, extended their hospitality, and Alberto Palleroni took me on some wild sand dune rides as we chased falcons around the island.

Dave Whitacre allowed me to accompany him to Guatemala and contributed to my knowledge of bat falcons, and Miguel Angel Vasquez led me through the jungles of Tikal and put up with my pidgin Spanish.

Mark Wexler of *National Wildlife* has contributed his support and friendship for the past twenty-eight years and expanded my knowledge of urban falcon nesting sites.

And lastly Tom Cade spent many hours introducing me into a world in which he is certainly a pioneer.

GEORGE HUEY

Biologists Stephen Hoffman and Alan Hinde examine a peregrine before its release.

HawkWatch International biologist Alan Hinde releases a peregrine falcon to return to its southern journey.

1
SKY HUNTER

The brown falcon of Australia, Tasmania, and New Guinea is a medium-large falcon that also hunts in pairs, likes to chase eagles, and loves to steal prey from peregrine nests.

FALCONS DIFFER FROM THE OTHER BIRDS OF PREY IN FORM AND HABIT. The falcon's silhouette is distinctive. In flight its wings are swept back, stiff, and tapered to a slender elliptical tip. A falcon's crown is high and beautifully contoured. Its feathers are sleek, shiny; its body muscular, as if it had just come from a gym. Most of the muscle is in the chest, to power the long, narrow wings.

Falcons also have a specially notched beak. Unlike other birds of prey, which kill their victims by binding to them and working their sharp talons into the vital organs, the falcon holds its prey with its talons while it uses its notched beak to kill with a sharp bite that severs the spinal cord.

Falcons lack the feathered fingers at the end of their wings that the harriers use to hover low over the marshes and the eagles and buteos (the red-tailed hawks, the broad-winged hawks, and so on) use to soar high in the canyons. Soaring is not the falcons' style of hunting, though they do soar occasionally. Falcons would rather perch on a high limb or cliff, wait for game to come into view, then expend their energy in high-speed aerial pursuit.

Speed is the falcons' forte. If birds of prey were airplanes, the eagles, the buteos, the kites, and the harriers would be the gliders, and the falcons would be the jets. High speed enables them to capture birds in midair. Most falcons prefer to capture their prey in the open — in a direct chase, an upward swoop, or a fast dive (stoop).

Accipiters (goshawks, Cooper's hawks, sharp-shinned hawks, etc.) take birds, too, but they do so in the forests, where their short wings and long tails give them the ability to swerve through the branches, taking their prey by stealth and surprise.

There are from twenty-five to forty species of falcons, according to different authorities. We present thirty-eight, based on ornithologists Tom Cade's and Nick Fox's most recent works on the subject. These falcon species range in size from the kestrel, some weighing under 3½ ounces (100 g), to the gyrfalcon, some weighing more than 4½ pounds (2 kg).

Though the fossil record of the falcon is poor, scientists speculate that a primitive kestrel falcon was the common ancestor of the falcon family. Since one of the characteristics of a falcon is to prey on birds in the open air, the kestrel, which takes birds in this way only occasionally, is perhaps the least evolved, whereas the peregrine, which takes almost all of its prey out of the sky, represents the apex of falcon evolution.

Scientists divide the falcons (genus *Falco*) into a number of groups or subgenera. There are thirteen kestrels that feed on insects, small rodents, and occasional birds. Though they may snatch prey in midair, kestrels are more apt to sit and wait, descending to the ground to take insects or rodents, or hovering over ground when there is no suitable perch.

Farther up the evolutionary ladder are the hobbies, which include the northern hobby, the African hobby, the Oriental hobby, the Australian hobby, the Eleonora's falcon, the sooty falcon, the western red-footed falcon, and the eastern red-footed falcon.

Hobbies are small to medium in size. They are the most agile of all falcons, taking small birds, large insects, and an occasional bat out of the air in a repertoire of straight-on, swooping, or diving attacks.

Merlins and red-headed falcons form their own subgenus. Merlins are small but fearless bird-eaters. They will doggedly circle up on a higher-flying bird until it is exhausted, and think nothing of blasting through a tight flock of birds (something that intimidates other falcons). The red-headed falcon is equally dashing but likes to hunt in pairs, one bird chasing the prey while the other comes in at another angle — cutting it off at the pass.

Scientists place the brown falcon of Australia, Tasmania, and New Guinea in its own subgenus. It is a medium-large falcon that also hunts in pairs, likes to chase eagles, and loves to steal prey from peregrine nests.

Scientists also put the orange-breasted falcon, the bat falcon, the aplomado falcon, and the New Zealand hobby in a separate subgenus,

Merlins will circle up on a higher-flying bird until it is exhausted, then attack.

principally on Nick Fox's supposition that all had a common southern hemispheric ancestor. Still, their habits are quite different. The bat falcon takes birds and insects in agile hobby-style acrobatics, while the New Zealand hobby is more apt to use direct-flying or tail-chasing attacks on birds and thinks nothing of occasionally binding onto a rabbit or hare that may weigh six times as much as the falcon.

The desert falcons — the gyrfalcon, the saker, the lanner, the laggar, the black falcon, the prairie falcon, and the gray falcon — are highly evolved large predators that have adapted to the dry mid-latitude and arctic deserts of the world. They have stronger feet and talons for capturing the larger reptiles, birds, and mammals.

The gyrfalcon, considered the ultimate status symbol of the Middle Ages' European potentates, makes its home in the Arctic, where its favorite food is the ptarmigan (a grouse-like bird), which it prefers to take in low, ground-hugging, Cruise-missile-style attacks. The saker, the banner bird of Attila the Hun, feeds mainly on small mammals, usually taking its prey near the ground in a series of shallow stoops, raking its victims with razor-sharp talons.

The larger falcons are all quite capable of taking animals three to four times their own weight. Sakers, like this one, were trained by Arab bedouin to go after small gazelles.

C. VOLPE/VIREO

The last, most highly evolved of the falcons is the peregrine — along with its very close cousin, the barbary falcon. The peregrine is a large falcon, but unlike its desert cousins the gyrfalcon, the saker, and the prairie, which take many mammals from the ground, the peregrine hunts birds almost exclusively from midair. The peregrine is to the sky what the great white shark is to the sea.

Historically, once the peregrine had adapted to its aerial ecological niche, it encountered little competition from other birds of prey and thus spread throughout the world. Only the merlin, another bird-eater, competes in the peregrine's circumpolar range, though the merlin is found only in the northern hemisphere. There are twenty-two subspecies of peregrines spread out over all the major continents, with the exception of Antarctica.

More has been written about the peregrine than about any other falcon, mostly because it was endangered, and because of its use in the sport of falconry. "It's also one of the most beautiful creatures on the planet," says Stephen Hoffman of HawkWatch International.

The peregrine falcon hunts birds almost exclusively from midair.

First Sightings

I remember the first time I ever saw a peregrine falcon in the wild. I was standing at the south rim of the Grand Canyon in Arizona, looking out onto the red, yellow, and orange layers of the sculptured buttes, pinnacles, and cliffs carved by the Colorado River. Swifts — small, speedy, acrobatic birds — filled the air of the upper canyon, zigzagging, banking, and darting back and forth in agile open-mouthed assaults on insects. But I was looking for another kind of flight display — the more direct, shallow, fluid, enormously powerful wing beat of the peregrine.

There are more than a hundred nesting pairs of peregrine falcons in the Grand Canyon, a number of which perch on the south rim.

I had memorized the description — slate back, auburn under-body, yellow eye ring, streamlined silhouette, curved beak, strong body, and long, narrow pointed wings. There were more than a hundred nesting pairs of peregrine falcons in the Grand Canyon, a number of which perched on the south rim, according to biologists. As I scanned the horizon, a falcon suddenly appeared not far above me. The dark vertical bars of its underside indicated it was a juvenile. I watched it fly over the edge, take a few dives at the swifts, and disappear over the rim. Swifts are a difficult quarry, especially for a juvenile, though falcons do capture them in the Grand Canyon.

The first time I ever saw a peregrine capture a bird in the wild was on Padre Island, off the coast of Texas. I remember the peregrine taking off from the shore and flying out over the water after a shorebird. It flew to a point above the bird and then dove full-speed at it, missing at first, swooping back up, diving, and hitting the bird with such force that it tumbled downward. The falcon swooped down and plucked it out of the sky.

PURE SPEED

All falcons are built with sleek aerodynamics. In a dive the falcon is shaped much like a teardrop or raindrop, nature's perfect design for friction-free descent. A falcon's nostrils have a whirled conch-like passage to slow air intake so the bird can breathe normally while flying very swiftly. Some biologists think that the falcon's nostrils may indeed function as a speedometer.

The Peregrine Fund's founding vice-chairman, Morley Nelson, recalled his first sighting of a peregrine in flight. Nelson was only twelve years old, out herding cattle on the family ranch in North Dakota in 1930, when he approached a pond to water his horse.

Seven teal ducks feeding on the pond rose into the air. Suddenly Nelson saw a peregrine falcon in a full 1,000-foot (300-m) vertical dive, jetting toward one of the ducks. The peregrine sliced through the duck with an explosion of feathers, then swooped out of its dive and plucked its prey from the air before it hit the ground.

"I just stood there in awe," remembers Nelson. "I couldn't believe anything could operate in such a graceful and tremendous way. I thought teal ducks were the fastest thing I'd ever seen, but the stoop [dive] of the falcon on its quarry is the fastest single action in nature."

Statistics uphold Nelson's conviction. Estimates of the maximum speed of a falcon dive are as fast as 273 miles an hour (440 km/h), based on analysis of motion-picture footage of a falcon in a full vertical dive taken by the Naval Research Laboratory in England in World War II. Most biologists, however, estimate the falcon's maximum velocity at 150 to 200 miles an hour (240 to 320 km/h), which is still faster than any other animal on earth.

The stoop of the falcon is a unique example of aerial coordination. Peregrine falcons nesting on the spires of the Cathedral of Cologne in Germany feed on jackdaws (small crows) as they fly across the

WAYNE NELSON

Biologists estimate the peregrine falcon's maximum velocity in the stoop (dive) at 150 to 200 miles an hour (240 to 320 km/h), which is faster than any other animal on earth.

A peregrine captures a duck.

Rhine River. To do this, the falcon moves off its perch just as the jackdaw starts over the water. The falcon gains altitude and then attacks just before the jackdaw reaches the other side. Once it folds back its wings to dive, the falcon is committed. It can't change its flight plan without opening its wings, slowing its speed, and throwing off its timing. The falcon must time its dive at the outset to connect with the moving bird a full 550 yards (500 m) away.

Some of the low, ground-hugging attacks of the desert falcons are equally coordinated. Lanners perch at comparative distances from North African watering holes, waiting for birds to land. They then launch low-level attacks that conceal their approach and that give the falcons another look at their prey only at the last instant when they attempt to strike.

Some biologists argue that the gyrfalcon is the fastest, while others say the prairie falcon is faster. Some assert that the large falcons may be faster in a dive but that the medium-size falcons (the merlin, the bat falcon, the hobby, or the rare taita falcon) may be the fastest in direct flapping flight.

In Guatemala, I watched two bat falcons approach me over the jungle, and though at first I could not distinguish their head-on silhouette, I knew instantly they were bat falcons by the incredible speed of their approach.

I watched two peregrine falcons test their marvelous flying abilities at a biological station at Point Reyes Seashore in northern California. The birds were hatched at the Predatory Bird Research Group in Santa Cruz, California, and released at a windy seaside cliff overlooking the Pacific, but stayed close to the release site, where the biologists continued to feed them until they'd learned to hunt for themselves. The falcons would roller-coaster across the sky in tandem, making occasional spectacular free-falls, keeping their wingtips together as they spiraled downward. They would make these incredibly fast dives, streaking past our observation post, a loud *whoosh* in their wake.

Most adults save this kind of energy-expending behavior for courtship or threat displays for other falcons. Wayne Nelson was observing peregrines on the Queen Charlotte Islands off Canada's west coast when a peregrine falcon he'd named the Masked Marauder decided to put on a threat display for a peregrine male that was intruding on his territory.

The Marauder took off from his cliff-top perch and chased the invader. "He had these deep wing beats — pump, pump, pump — slow and powerful as opposed to the normal shallow ones. After chasing for about a mile, the Marauder suddenly went into a power flying display, pumping while he was climbing and diving, saw-toothing his way across the sky, and making very sharp turns, all the while twisting and pumping. And when he finally returned to the nest cliff, he came up over the cliff, stooped almost vertically, and landed gently on a tall tree. I just wanted to jump up and shout, it was so incredible."

Tom Cade watched a gyrfalcon display next to the Colville River in Alaska. The falcon flew in enormous undulating loops across the cliff face while rotating from side to side. The sun, reflecting off its brighter belly, made flashes that could be seen for miles.

Tactics of Predator and Prey

Falcons are attackers, not searchers. Unlike eagles, harriers, and vultures, they don't soar looking for prey. Falcons have a smaller wing area relative to weight. It's a faster wing that requires more energy to fly — they don't have the feathered wingtip "fingers" that help the eagle, the vulture, and some hawks soar but that cut down on speed.

The larger falcons are all quite capable of taking animals three to four times their own weight. For example, sakers were trained by ancient Arab bedouin to go after houbara bustards (a Middle Eastern bird as large as a turkey) and even small gazelles. Most falcons, though, reserve their efforts to capture smaller prey. Though they may grab smaller birds out of the air, often they will let the larger birds fall to the ground and then attack them in a series of short swooping dives. According to Scott Francis, a biologist who observed this on Padre Island, "they'll run up in the air 30 or 40 feet [10 to 12 m] and then come back down, throw the feet out and smack it in the head until the bird is unconscious or dead."

Unlike hawks and eagles, which bind to their prey, killing with long, sharp talons, most of the larger falcons use their great speed and precision to strike the bird with their feet in a karate-like blow. The falcon is blessed with specially cushioned joints and high-tensile-strength bone to withstand such an impact.

Several falconers tell of being knocked out in this fashion by their own birds demanding food. They describe the blow as a close-fisted

WAYNE NELSON

A peregrine takes off from a cliff-top perch and chases after an invader.

Peregrines are the fastest aerial predators. This one stands over its quarry, a plover.

backhand or straight punch that is delivered by extending the feet at the last instant of the dive. However, slow-motion films of a falcon's 40-mile-per-hour (50-km/h) attack show the bird delivering a glancing blow with open claws in which the rear talon may serve to rake its victim. Attacks can be much faster than 40 miles an hour. If the falcon is diving at a speed faster than 100 miles an hour (160 km/h), a mere touch of a talon on the prey's head may stun or kill it. Falcons have loose, limp, comparatively weak toes that might otherwise break with the force of such a blow.

Falcons also have binocular vision that may be from three to eight times more powerful than a human's. Prairie falcons circle from 1,000 to 2,000 feet (300 to 600 m) high over the Idaho desert and from that distance are able to spot Townsend's ground squirrels as they leave their holes and to determine whether the squirrel has ventured far enough from the hole for the falcon to attempt a kill. With a telescope, Wayne Nelson watched a peregrine falcon in the Yukon take off in a long, shallow, pumping dive to attack a robin-size bird among the treetops just over two miles (3 km) from the falcon's hunting perch. "To see something that small at that distance, decide what it is and when to take off to try to capture it is truly amazing," said Nelson.

Prey use a number of strategies to avoid the falcon. One way is to escape into the trees or brush where most falcons will not pursue — high-speed impact with a branch can be fatal. Australia's black falcon uses blood-curdling screams and rapid stoops to frighten its prey out of cover.

Some birds will form a tight flock, which the falcon avoids because of the possibility of injury from a collision, though the strategy does not always work. Lynn Oliphant, professor of veterinary anatomy at the University of Saskatchewan, observed a flock of about a thousand Bohemian waxwings suddenly gather in a tight flock, shifting back and forth nervously. He saw a merlin circle up into the sky, turn, and dive right through the flock.

Another strategy that prey use is to try to out-climb the falcon. Since a falcon's wings are not designed for soaring, herons, egrets, and shorebirds, with their broader soaring wings, often have the advantage. On Padre Island, biologist Alberto Palleroni and I watched a flock of egrets suddenly tighten up when a falcon approached. The falcon was careful to keep the flock upwind. The egrets couldn't use the wind to their advantage, since to fly with the wind would take them to the falcon, so they chose to out-soar him and started to climb.

A mere touch of a talon on the prey's head may stun or kill it if the falcon is diving at a speed of more than 100 miles an hour (160 km/h).

The falcon flew beneath them and began a determined chase, circling the flock in wide arcs to gain altitude. After a number of 45-degree dives it finally hit one of the egrets, which plummeted to the ground, the falcon directly behind.

Sometimes the prey will change tactics and try to race the peregrine to the ground in a search for cover. On the Yukon River near the Canada–Alaska border, Tom Cade, founding chairman of the Peregrine Fund, watched a shorebird suddenly give up on a high circling chase, fold its wings, and dive for the safety of the forest below, but the falcon, which can dive much faster, caught up with the bird and snatched it out of the air, just above the trees.

Most falcons are loners, but a few species, such as the Eleonora's falcon, hunt in groups. (This falcon was named after one of the most famous women of the fourteenth century, Eleonora of Arborea, who distinguished herself as a military leader, regent, and judge in Sardinia.)

Unlike most falcons, which nest in spring, Eleonora's falcons nest in fall, when as many as 5 billion songbirds migrate to Africa across the Mediterranean. Then these falcons gorge on the hoopoes, golden orioles, and other songbirds weakened by grueling nonstop flights of 600 miles (1000 km) over continuous waterway. On the islands of Paximada, Mogador, and Majorca, Eleonor's falcons abandon their solitary ways and form tight nesting colonies to prey on the migrating birds.

At daybreak, the male falcons leave the females and the young and rise into the updraft above the water in positions from sea level to 3,000 feet (1000 m), virtually filling the air space around the island, forming a falcon wall. Migrants that stray into the wall are subjected to a barrage of attacks from all directions, each driving the bird lower until it is caught or until it touches the water, where it loses control and is easily taken. Despite the perils of the falcon wall, most birds sail through, and no species has been recorded suffering more than 1 percent casualties. Nature has a way with checks and balances.

Not all hunters return with prey, though some falcons are better hunters than others. Hunting success measured by biologists in the

At daybreak male Eleonora's falcons leave their breeding grounds in the islands of the Mediterranean and position themselves from sea level to 3,000 feet (1000 m) in the air, forming a predatory wall that migrant songbirds must confront.

wild can vary from 7 to 62 percent. The exception was the Red Baron, a male peregrine falcon released from a falcon reintroduction program managed by Tom Cade at Cornell University and monitored by Marty Gilroy, now the Eastern Recovery Coordinator for the Peregrine Fund.

In 1978 Gilroy recorded 81 of the Baron's hunts, with 73 percent ending in capture. In 1979 the Baron caught 95 birds in 102 hunts, a 93 percent success rate. In that year he also had an amazing run of 68 consecutive hunts in 44 days without a miss.

The Red Baron hunted from a New Jersey marsh and took blue jays that migrated down the eastern seaboard. "He was in top shape," said Gilroy, "sleeker looking than most falcons, broad at the shoulder and slender at the waist. You could tell when he meant business — his feathers would be all preened, and he'd be looking east, crouched down and ready to blast off."

The Red Baron would dive at a flock of jays, usually deliberately missing with the first pass, looking for the one that would panic and separate from the flock. The Baron would then loop back up and snatch the chosen victim. "He had more finesse than other peregrines. He'd lived there awhile, learned about his prey, and chosen the best tactics. He'd done his homework," said Gilroy.

In a new age of environmental awareness we are just beginning to understand the role falcons play as a predator in the food chain. Unlike humans who kill wantonly, falcons will take no more than normal population growth will allow. Falcons take the weaker, the sicker, the less adaptive birds, so that there is a selective pressure on the prey population to get better, faster, and healthier. Our greatest challenge is understanding that role and, perhaps, learning a lesson from it.

The Australian hobby feeds mainly on birds (some larger than itself) and some insects and bats, which it takes mostly from the air in a swift stoop.

Opposite:
The Old World or common kestrel preys on insects, small mammals, small birds, and lizards.

PETER STEYN

The lesser kestrel, perhaps the most social of all falcons, feeds in flocks, scouring the steppe and forest-steppe of Eurasia and North Africa for insects and an occasional reptile or small bird.

2
THE SPORT OF KINGS

HISTORICALLY, NO BIRD OF PREY HAS SHARED AS CLOSE A RELATIONSHIP with humans as the falcon did during the Middle Ages when the sport of falconry was the rage of Europe's and Asia's feudal lords, princes, and potentates. Falconry was also known as "hawking" because falcons were not the only birds flown at game. Knights took their favorite birds to church so often that eventually rules were made to bar them. A few couples even got married with falcons on their fists.

Falcons were also part of the spoils of war. In 1396, during one of Christendom's more catastrophic crusades, the Ottoman Sultan Beyazid captured the son of Philip the Bold, duke of Burgundy. The duke offered 200,000 gold ducats to get his offspring back. Instead the sultan demanded and got something even more valuable — twelve white gyrfalcons.

Falconry was also popular among the clergy. Pope Leo x was constantly in the field hawking, and was even chastised by Charles d'Arcussia, the Italian who was falconer to Louis XIII of France, for too loudly berating his comrades during a flight. Nuns had a particular fondness for falconry and would take their birds with them into chapel. William of Wykeham, bishop of Winchester, complained that the practice interfered with the services.

Falcons accompanied their masters to battle and were an integral part of the trappings of English armies. During the Hundred Years' War, falcons crossed the Channel to the battles of Crécy, Poitiers, and Agincourt. When Edward III invaded France, he had thirty falconers with him, according to one historian.

In the sixteenth century the Mogul emperor Akbar of southern Asia was another devotee of falconry. Before launching a new army

During the Middle Ages the sport of falconry was the rage of Europe's and Asia's feudal lords, princes, and potentates. Here falconers and their birds are shown in a Florentine painting of the procession of the Magi.

campaign, he organized large-scale hunting parties so that his military might go through their exercises chasing animals.

In Akbar's day, Raja Rudradeva of Kumaon wrote his treatise *The Art of Hunting*, in which he dwelt on the pleasure of the sport: "The enjoyment of hunting is more exquisite than even the enjoyment of women. For the pleasures of hunting fascinate and draw away even the husband of the woman whose eyes resemble those of the frightened stags. If enjoyment were not so exquisite then why should men forsake their mistresses clinging to their necks, and go abroad in cold nights?"

According to Rudradeva, hunting and falconry were considered the last of the "eighteen addictions," along with fault-finding, gambling, dancing, and sleeping during the day. To the raja, all these addictions had their usefulness when "practiced within proper bounds," but "too much addiction to them must be avoided."

In Japan falconry was so popular that vast game reserves were maintained. Around the turn of the seventeenth and eighteenth centuries, samurai warriors were issued a military manual that included a fairly thorough treatise on falconry.

SCALA/ART RESOURCE, NEW YORK

Falconry was also practiced in the Middle East. According to one Arabic tradition, the first falconer was a king of Persia, who captured a bird, kept it near him, and learned many good lessons from his falcon.

BEGINNINGS

The history of falconry goes far back. According to one Japanese work, falcons were among the presents made to Chinese princes in the time of the Hsia dynasty, which began in the twenty-first century B.C. There is evidence that falconry was practiced by the peoples of ancient India, Assyria, Sumeria, Babylonia, Egypt, and Persia more than a thousand years before Rome came into existence.

According to one Arabic tradition, the first falconer was a king of Persia. The king was on an excursion one day and watched a wild falcon rise from its perch to take a passing bird. Having made a meal of it, the falcon flew down to the river to drink and bathe before returning to a tree.

The king was "struck with admiration at its majestic appearance, its wonderful patience, and its power over other birds, which it seemed to take by sovereignty of nature." He decided to have that bird. The king had the falcon snared and tied to a perch he kept near him, and learned many good lessons from the bird. According to legend, the once-violent king, inspired by the falcon, became a calmer, wiser sovereign.

Another tradition has it that Ulysses brought falconry to Greece after the siege of Troy, although most historians believe that falconry was introduced to Europeans by Attila and his Huns who stormed into Europe in the fifth century A.D. Falconry was taken up by the Lombards, a people who settled in northern Italy about 560, and the sport spread rapidly. By 875 it was practiced throughout western Europe and Saxon England.

Falcons were protected under English law. Anyone who destroyed falcons' eggs could be imprisoned for a year, and anyone who poached a falcon from the wild might have an eye poked out. Perhaps no such stringent laws have ever been passed to protect a wild bird or animal. Indeed, one could say that wildlife conservation was born during the age of falconry.

St. Bavon was almost a victim of the legal stringency rampant throughout Europe in the Middle Ages. He was a native of Halle, in Belgium, where he lived in the seventh century. According to legend he was accused of stealing a white gyrfalcon, tried for the offense, and condemned to be executed. On the day and at the place of his execution, the missing falcon suddenly appeared in the air and came down to land. St. Bavon's innocence established by a sign from heaven caused him to be released immediately. He subsequently came to be regarded as the patron saint of falconers.

THE FALCON EMPEROR

Frederick II of Hohenstaufen, Holy Roman emperor, king of Sicily and Jerusalem, brought the sport to its highest state of respectability when he wrote *De Arte Venandi cum Avibus* (*The Art of Falconry*) in the latter part of his reign from 1210 to 1250. To Frederick, falconry was "the noblest of sports." The work was six volumes long, the culmination of thirty years of intensely active interest and preparation. As the first scientific treatise on birds, it marked him as one of the founders of ornithology.

Frederick was obsessed with falconry. He is said to have failed disastrously in one important military campaign because he went hawking instead of pressing the siege of a fortress. His crusade of 1228 influenced his book. From it he brought back expert falconers and their falcons from Syria and Arabia and spent many of his leisure hours learning from them the secrets of their art. It took him eleven

Gyrfalcons were a popular bird of royalty, but they were difficult to train.

years to write *De Arte* with the help of his son Manfred in his beloved Apulian estates in southeast Italy, where he owned not only many magnificent hunting lodges but also at least one castle especially built for his falcons.

De Arte was far more than a dissertation on hunting. It described in detail the anatomy of birds, the pneumaticity of the bones, the form of the sternum, structure of the lungs, and mechanical conditions of flight, as well as nesting and migratory habits. Frederick described at length all manner of falcon training and falconry apparatus, such as the falconer's bag in which he carries the falcon's lure and food, and the falconer's glove, which should be large and of thick leather. He also gave handy hints for falconers, such as how to quiet a restless falcon by spraying it with mouthfuls of pure cold water — though the falconer must thoroughly cleanse his mouth before the operation.

Frederick was also a purist. Hunting for food for the falconer put too great a burden on a falcon. He believed falconry was best practiced as an art, whose aim was the rearing and owning of the best birds, and he cautioned that a successful falconer cannot be "indolent or careless, for this art requires much labor and much study."

Besides Frederick II's *De Arte*, a number of medieval treatises were written on falconry, among them *Falconry in Two Books* (1615) by Symon Latham, *The Booke of Faulconrie or Hawking* (1575) by George Turberville, and *An Approved Treatise of Hawks and Hawking* (1619) by Edmund Bert, which are today studied both for their advice on the sport and for their insight into medieval customs and lore.

In his book Bert gives such advice as "how to reclaime a Hawke that will neither abide horse-men, strangers, carts, or women, or such like," and also suggests "a powder to be given to a Hawke that bloweth and is short-winded." Today's falconers use much the same quaint medicines and have the same names for falcon problems as those Bert once described.

To Tame a Falcon

Young falcons to be trained for falconry were taken from the nest only after all their down had been replaced by brown feathers yet before the falcon had learned to fly. They were placed in an artificial nest and fed on freshly killed bird, rabbit, rat, or squirrel.

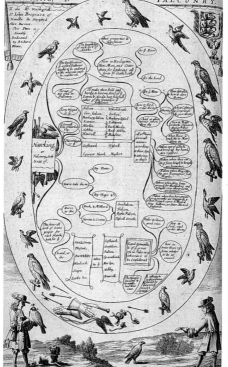

Falconry was especially popular in Britain from the tenth century on. This illustration of falconers and their birds is a frontispiece from The Gentleman's Recreation, *published in 1686.*

The basic equipment used in falconry has not changed over the years. A lure (a padded weight covered with wings), hoods, and other essentials are featured in these illustrations from an eighteenth-century book.

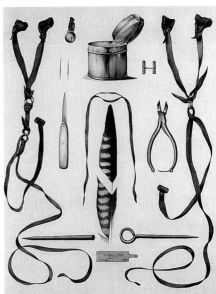

At first the young falcons were not confined, but had bells tied around their necks to help the falconer locate them should they fly away, and wore "jesses," small leather leg straps that hung loose, though they could later be attached to a leash. The birds were then "at hack," an English term for the buckboard-style taxi that was often used as a platform upon which their food was placed.

The falconer would feed the birds secretly so they would not be aware that the food came from humans. Soon the birds would be making long flights into the surrounding country, testing their flying abilities and going after wild game. When the falcon began to be absent at the regular feeding time, the falconer captured the bird back with nets, placed a hood over its head, tied a swivel and leash to its jesses, and left the bird on a block perch to settle down. Then began one of the falconer's most difficult missions — getting the bird used to humans.

The falcon was carried on the gloved hand of the falconer for several hours each day, spoken to, and softly stroked until it began to lose its nervousness and to become reconciled to the hand as a perch. The falcon was fed with its hood still on until it ate without hesitation. Then gradually the hood was removed and the bird allowed to eat by candle-light. Later it ate by sunlight, as it slowly became accustomed to men, women, children, and dogs.

Eventually the bird was taken into the field, where it was introduced to the lure, a padded weight with wings and with a long string attached. Food was tied to the lure and the falcon allowed to eat from it until the bird associated the lure with food. The falconer manipulated the falcon's diet so that the bird was in peak health but just hungry enough to come to the falconer and the lure when called. Gradually the falconer worked with the lure and the bird, sometimes twirling it about his head while the bird took practice dives at it. These were the first cautious moments when the bird was allowed to fly free as the falconer tested how their bond had grown. If the bond was not sufficient or if the falconer was not patient enough with the initial training, the bird might fly away and never return.

An illustration from Birds of North America *(1903) shows a peregrine with a successfully captured duck.*

When the bird had become accustomed to the lure, it was allowed to go after game. At first it was tested on pigeons or doves, but thereafter it was flown at ducks or other more difficult prey. When the falcon captured prey, the falconer used the lure to entice the bird back. Often if the falcon was on a bird, the falconer would put the lure beside it, give the string a few jerks, and the falcon would go to the more active lure. Sometimes the falconer would place the lure on top of the prey, or exchange the lure for the prey. Then, while the bird was eating, the falconer would attach its leash and replace its hood.

Falconers would also train older birds that they netted as adults. These birds were easier to teach to hunt, since they didn't need to be fed at hack, but they required a much longer period of initial training. The falcon had to be redeemed through immense patience from a state of hatred and suspicion of all men to one of acceptance.

Falcons were kept in the "mews," which could be anything from a makeshift cage to a separate room in the palace, depending on who owned the bird. Much of the same language of falconry is still used by modern-day falconers. An "eyess" is the name for a falcon taken from the nest. A "haggard" is a bird captured as an adult. The "pitch" of a falcon is the height to which it rises before descending on its prey.

In falconry only the larger female hawk is properly called the falcon. A male, which is smaller than the female by up to one-third, is the tiercel. Falconry is still very much a part of the English language. "Debonair" is a French falconers' term for "of good wind or air." The gorge of a falcon is a pocket in the neck where the bird stores food not yet digested. Thus a person "gorged" is exceptionally full. A "boozer" is a falcon that drank all the water. The carrier of the "cadge," on which the hawks were perched, was usually a country boy or an old man, and from this came "cadger," "codger," and doubtless "cad." From "haggard" comes "hag," an older bird set in its ways.

Finding New Birds

In the Middle Ages, finding new birds was as important an endeavor as taking care of the old. Falcons from Scandinavia were considered especially good birds. Falcons from Iceland and Greenland were sent to the royal mews in Norway and Denmark. From there, surplus falcons were sold to a medieval company in Lübeck in northern Germany and then shipped across the Alps to Venice and thence to Alexandria, Baghdad, and Constantinople.

Frederick ɪɪ's *De Arte* gave detailed instructions for transporting the birds over long distances. They were to be carried on a cadge — a box-like frame suspended from the shoulders of a man, with falcons perched on padded bars. According to Frederick, the falcons should have their eyes sealed shut, and in summer and autumn should preferably be transported at night to avoid the heat of the day and the nervous distraction of other birds singing. In the event of rain, the falconer should take the brunt of it himself to protect his precious cargo.

Falcons were also captured in the open moor of Valkenswaard, Holland, where each year millions of migrant birds would stop on their way south, followed by the falcons that preyed on them. All during the Middle Ages falcons were trapped and trained here for the nobility of Europe. In the fall, knights and falconers from the courts of every feudal lord and king would gather for lively medieval auctions, bidding against one another for the best of the birds captured that year.

Falcons as Status Symbols

For most, falconry had two purposes. It was a way of hunting for food, and it was also a means of entertainment and sport. The yeoman and the burgher flew goshawks and sparrowhawks at rabbits, pheasants, and other game on the ground. The birds were carried on their arms, and when game was sighted, the bird flew straight at its quarry. The French called the goshawk the "cuisinier," as its principal function was keeping the stomach full.

The long-winged falcons — the gyrfalcon, the lanner, the saker, and especially the peregrine — were flown to entertain kings and queens, dukes and duchesses. These falcons were flown at higher-flying game such as ducks, rooks, and herons. The birds were sent

According to the Boke of Saint Albans, *the sparrowhawk was for the priest.*

Merlins were "milady's falcon." Mary Queen of Scots was an ardent fan of the merlins and was occasionally released from imprisonment for short excursions with her falcons.

Right:
During the reign of Louis XIII *of France, the royal mews were filled with falcons, including kestrels.*

Far right:
Peregrines were the most frequently used bird for falconry. They were not only easily trained but provided the most daring spectacles.

aloft, where they would circle high up while the dogs and beaters worked through the brush, trying to flush the game. Once a bird was flushed, the falcon would go into a stoop, striking the game in a display of aerial gymnastics.

Keeping the falcons for the nobility and the goshawks for the lower classes was a part of the Middle Ages' social order. According to the *Boke of Saint Albans* of 1486, written by Dame Juliana Barnes, the prioress of Sopwell nunnery near St. Albans, England, there was a type of bird of prey for each class of feudal society. The golden eagle was for the emperor; the gyrfalcon for the king; the female peregrine for the prince; the rock falcon (another form of peregrine) for the duke; the typical peregrine for the earl; the male peregrine for the baron; the saker for the knight; the lanner for the squire; the merlin for the lady; the hobby for the page or yeoman; the male goshawk for the poor man; the female sparrowhawk for the priest; and the male sparrowhawk for the holywater clerk.

To keep a falcon that was above one's station was a felony regarded as an act of defiance against the established social order and also a potential threat to a valuable wildlife resource, making good birds harder and more expensive to get for those for whom they were intended. According to the *Boke*, cutting off the hands of people who kept falcons above their station proved to be an "excellent deterrent" to this crime.

SPECIES OF FALCONS USED IN FALCONRY

Peregrines were the most frequently used bird for falconry. They were not only easily trained but provided the most daring spectacle. Still, other falcons had their place.

Merlins were "milady's falcon." They were sent after high-flying skylarks, which they captured in a chase in which the merlin flew upward in tight circles until it was high enough to dive back on the skylark or was out-flown by the lark. Mary Queen of Scots was an ardent fan of the merlins, and Elizabeth I occasionally let her out of the dungeon for short hawking excursions.

Lanners and sakers were used, though most often by Mideastern royalty. The Afghans had a peculiar penchant for hawking with large birds after large game. They sometimes hunted wild sheep with an eagle and a saker — the eagle hovering over the sheep, the saker binding to the sheep's head, and the hunter delivering the killing blow with his knife.

Gyrfalcons were a popular bird of royalty, but they were difficult to train. Swedish naturalist Olaus Magnus wrote in 1555 that the gyrfalcon "was the most noble bird of all." Their value was heightened by the fact that they came from the Arctic, which Marco Polo

This detail from a painted Florentine hunting chest reflects some of the interest in falconry that was spreading throughout Europe.

described as "the Region of Darkness" and which medieval people viewed as a mysterious and evil place.

Edward I in 1276 received eight gray and three white gyrfalcons from the king of Norway as a sign of peace. After England and Russia established diplomatic relations in 1552, Czar Ivan IV (the Terrible) sent Queen Mary I (Bloody Mary) "a large and faire Jerfawcon," and the queen reciprocated with "a male and female lion."

THE ROYAL HUNT

Marco Polo attests to the aristocratic fascination with the falcon in the Middle Ages when in his memoirs of the Far East he fails to mention tea, printed books, and the Great Wall of China, but dwells lovingly on the gyrfalcons of Kublai Khan, founder of the Mongol dynasty of China.

When the great khan traveled, he was accompanied by "full ten thousand falconers, who carry with them a vast number of gyrfalcons, peregrine falcons, and sakers." The khan had his favorites, but, like the ruler of a large harem, he had a number of executive falconers always out searching for new talent.

Royal hunting parties were then massive affairs performed completely for show. Falconers and other servants did all the legwork: flushing the game, bringing up the falcons, picking up the quarry. Royalty did little else but release the falcon at the last second and then sit back and enjoy the show.

Falconry was especially popular in Britain from the tenth century on, and every British chieftain kept a large number of birds. In those days the master of the hawks was the fourth officer in rank and dignity, and sat in the fourth place from his sovereign at the royal table. Still, he was permitted no more than three drafts of ale, lest he become intoxicated and neglect his birds. When the master of the hawks was unusually successful in a hunt, the prince was obliged by law and custom to rise and receive him as he entered the hall, and sometimes to hold the master's stirrup as he alighted from his horse. Falconry came to its climax in the early 1600s, with the last of the

This illustration shows a hunting party and their falcons, as well as some herons, the results of a successful hunt.

great European falconer kings, Louis XIII of France. Many of the lords of his court owed their position to falconry. Under Louis, the Royal Falconry Establishment became a miniature state forming a sort of feathered court around the king. Louis was famous for leading hawking expeditions when he was only six years old, and by the age of ten he was proficient at training falcons.

During his reign, the royal mews were filled with peregrines, gyrfalcons, merlins, goshawks, sparrowhawks, hobbies, and kestrels. The king and his falconers, among whom was Charles d'Arcussia, author of several books on falconry, trained falcons to hunt in trios, a difficult task since falcons are by nature solitary hunters. With this trio he could go after gray herons — big, powerful water birds — which were then still plentiful and considered a delicacy.

Louis even composed a ballet, *La Merlaison*, about the pleasures of sending falcons after blackbirds and thrushes. Under his royal sponsorship, hawking retinues, both big and small, became quite numerous. Peasants and lords alike hawked for pleasure or fashion, or to be noticed by the king. The French Revolution, accompanied by the breaking up of feudal domains into smaller holdings and the reclaiming of large areas of wild land, ultimately put an end to a thousand years of falconry. The invention of buckshot made falconry a less productive way to obtain fowl for the table.

THE END OF AN ERA

When the popularity of the sport faded, people began to regard falcons as competition for game and later as pests. However, falconry was preserved by a few English and European hawking clubs. In Great Britain the Falconers Society of England was founded in 1770 and stayed active until 1838. Colonel Thornton of Thornville Royal, who was instrumental in its beginning, was certainly one of its most colorful characters. According to one journalist, Thornton used to go hunting with "fourteen servants with hawks on their wrists, ten hunters, a pack of staghounds and lap-dog beagles, and a brace of wolves." Legend has it that he was also accompanied by a mistress who was quite a good horsewoman, an accomplishment considered risqué at that time in England. Thornton allegedly bet on his mistress in races and engaged in public brawls with her competitors in the racetrack grandstand at York.

A falconer poses proudly with his birds in this 1833 English painting.

FALCONRY TODAY

Falconry today is practiced by a small contingent of men and women who consider the sport exciting enough to put the time and effort into it. In many ways it has remained the same. Falconers still train birds much as their predecessors did a thousand years ago, though some of the equipment is different. The jess on the falcon's leg has been replaced by a shorter cuff and removable trailing piece of leather. Radio transmitters are frequently used to relocate birds, perhaps the ultimate refinement of the bell.

Many of the falcons flown in falconry in North America and Europe are now bred in captivity. Hybrids, combining the traits of such species as the gyrfalcon, the lanner, the prairie, the saker, and the peregrine, are now a common result of artificial insemination.

Falcon hunts are more often solitary ventures with a falconer and the bird. Sometimes friends gather for comradeship, and occasional meets draw falconers from afar. For the most part falconry has become the sport of a small, devoted contingent of the middle class rather than the aristocracy.

Only in the Middle East is falconry practiced with any of the fanfare that it was accorded during the Middle Ages. Falconry is particularly popular with modern-day sheiks on the Arabian Peninsula. One sheik was so fond of the sport that he had a bed made in the shape of a falcon's foot. One talon mechanically uncurled to become a staircase to the mattress while another talon held a TV.

In Dubai, capital of the United Arab Emirates, next to Saudi Arabia, is one of the most advanced avian hospitals in the world designed especially for falcons. The hospital was set up by Sheik Hamdan Maktoum, a member of Dubai's ruling family and an ardent falconer. It is run by two veterinarians from the United States, Cheryl and David Remple, who formerly worked to rescue endangered peregrines in Wyoming.

In 1976, at the invitation of Sheik Zayd bin Sultan Al Nihayyan, the first International Conference on Falconry was held in Abu Dhabi. The occasion was the fifth anniversary of the foundation of the United Arab Emirates. Eighty countries from North America, western Europe, and the Far and Middle East accepted the invitation and were royally entertained. Prominent among the delegations were the Japanese, who demonstrated falconry in magnificent traditional garb.

SKIPP TUBBS/PHOTO RESEARCHERS

Sometimes falconers gather for comradeship, but falcon hunts are more often solitary ventures with only the falconer and his bird.

Today French falconers are organized under the Association nationale des fauconniers et autoursiers français and German ones under the Deutscher Falkenorden, founded in 1923 with the enthusiastic support of Hermann Göring. It is said that he designed the German dive-bomber — which dove low to drop its bomb load — after observing the stoop of the falcon.

In England falconers gather under the British Falconers' Club and in the U.S. and Canada under the North American Falconers Association. In North America the number of falconers was small early in this century. World War II veterans helped to stimulate interest in the sport. Even though falconry has no traditional ties in North America, its falconers' club has become one of the most active in the world, with a membership today of more than 3,000.

The Controversy

On December 17, 1982, Marcus Ciesielski, then nineteen, and Lothar Ciesielski arrived at Kennedy International Airport in New York with three gyrfalcons and three prairie falcons, captured on the Montana prairie in the United States. The brothers turned the birds over to François Messouadene, who had in his possession seven first-class tickets — presumably one for each bird and one for himself — for a flight to Riyadh, the Saudi capital.

Unbeknownst to the parties involved, their actions were carefully monitored by the U.S. Fish and Wildlife Service as part of a three-year investigation known as Operation Falcon. According to the service, the two brothers were part of an international black market in birds of prey. Some of the major players in this black market were also connected with a Canadian company called Birds of Prey International, which had reportedly sold $750,000 worth of raptors over two years. The Saudis were said to be paying up to $100,000 apiece for healthy birds of prey.

During the course of the investigation some thirty-nine arrests were made and some prestigious falconers and even falcon biologists were investigated. Both the U.S. Peregrine Fund, an eminent raptor breeding facility then based at Cornell University, and the Wainwright Endangered Species Facility of the Canadian Wildlife Service had their breeding programs audited. Suddenly, falconers in Europe and North America found themselves under the scrutiny of the law.

The U.S. Fish and Wildlife effort relied heavily on the testimony of an undercover agent, Jeffrey McPartlin, who had been convicted of smuggling two gray gyrfalcons out of the country in 1972. During the course of the operation McPartlin presented illegally caught falcons to falconers. Many of those arrested said McPartlin repeatedly called them with offers for birds, often lowering the price if they refused. As one Texas attorney said, "It's like having someone bring Marilyn Monroe by and ask if she can spend the night."

Most of the small-timers were charged with felonies and allowed to plead guilty to misdemeanors. Lothar Ciesielski and François Messouadene were let off, but Marcus Ciesielski was fined $10,000 and made to leave the country.

There is still a lot of controversy surrounding Operation Falcon. Falconers and falcon biologists contend that there is little illegal

A. PALLERONI

Some argue that falconry is a blood sport, equivalent to cock fighting, while others say it is an advanced form of bird watching.

trafficking of falcons. They point out that McPartlin was himself turned in by almost a dozen falconers during his investigation. They also point to a study the U.S. Fish and Wildlife Service conducted after Operation Falcon that concluded that both the legal and the illegal take of falcons in that country had no influence on the wild population. There is, however, some concern in Europe that a black market fostered by high prices paid by Arab falconers may be having a detrimental effect.

Tom Cade estimates that Arab falconers trap perhaps 2,000 saker falcons each year. He contends that the birds are trapped in their first autumn when almost half would normally die from natural causes during their first year. He estimates that there are perhaps 20,000 to 100,000 pairs of wild sakers in the world and that this take does not affect population stability.

Apparently no take by falconers, legal or illegal, has had anywhere near the effect that pesticides and habitat loss have had on certain species.

To some environmentalists falconry is objectionable even if it doesn't affect wildlife populations. They argue that falconry is a "blood sport" equivalent to cock fighting. But falconry is a method of hunting that requires innumerable hours to prepare a bird for the hunt, and that even on its best days will be far less successful than if the hunter had used a gun. Further, the falcon takes far fewer quarry when trained and flown in falconry than it would if it were in the wild. Its life expectancy in captivity is much higher. Whenever it is flown, the trained falcon can and sometimes does return to the wild. The joy in falconry is in viewing the natural predatory act of the falcon, something the bird would be doing even without the falconer there to watch. Falconers argue that in this sense their sport is simply an advanced type of bird watching.

The simple fact is that falconers have developed most of the methods for breeding hawks and falcons in captivity. They have also been the backbone of the worldwide effort to bring back the peregrine falcon from its endangered status. Well over half of the biologists and volunteers who have worked with this bird in one of the most massive recovery efforts in the history of wildlife management have been falconers. I am neither a falconer nor a hunter, but after seeing the evidence I must admit that without falconers and falconry there would be far fewer nesting peregrine falcons in the world today.

Falcons and dogs wait for the hunt preparations to begin.

Left:
Black falcons shown here are used for falconry. Many of the birds flown in falconry are now bred in captivity.

Opposite:
The gyrfalcon occasionally migrates south in winter and feeds almost entirely on seabirds.

3
THE SEASON OF AWAKENING

SPRING IS THE BEGINNING OF LIFE FOR MOST YOUNG FALCONS, WHETHER in the northern or southern hemisphere. Spring brings an explosion of new life from the plants, insects, and smaller birds, and nature times the hatching of the young falcons to this season of plenty.

Near the equator, where the seasons are not so distinct, falcons take advantage of other rhythms. The African hobby begins laying its eggs at the end of the dry season, which can be in October in South Africa or April in Kenya, so that the young are fledged about two months later when the flying insects and small birds are most abundant.

Except for the timing and duration of individual events, falcon nesting behavior is quite similar among the species. Many male gyrfalcons over-winter in Iceland and begin their flashing territorial displays in January or early February. Migrating falcons may return later, but the series of events is similar. First the male stakes out territory, then courtship begins, followed by nesting, and the breeding season concludes when the young falcons learn to fly and hunt by themselves.

Whether the birds separate for the nonbreeding season and pair up only on the nesting grounds depends somewhat on the species and the local situation. Migratory peregrine falcons, which breed in North America, have been observed in pairs on their nonbreeding grounds in South America, though it is still uncertain if these pairs are the original nesting birds. In other areas where prey are available year-round, peregrines do not migrate to warmer climates for the winter but remain on the nesting territory or close by as loosely knit pairs.

The aplomado falcon of Central and South America stays paired year-round, as does Australia's brown falcon, though it is thought that most pairs go their separate ways after the young have abandoned the

American kestrels prefer tight entrances to their nests to protect their young from larger predators.

nesting area and no longer rely on their parents for food.

Falcons are normally nonsocial. Nesting along a river or a coastal palisade, they might space themselves five to ten miles (8 to 15 km) or more apart, but at the breeding grounds on the Queen Charlotte Islands off the Pacific Coast of Canada, the Snake River in Idaho in the United States, and the islands of Paximada and Mogador in the Mediterranean Sea, things are unusually congested.

The Queen Charlottes, a group of about 150 islands, have temperate rainforests and bogs surrounded by craggy volcanic rocks and sandy beaches that rise to steep cliffs. In late winter, the peregrine falcons begin to spend less time perching in the forest fringing the islands and more time on or near the palisade nesting sites that skirt the rocky island shores. They stake out territories that range from approximately one-half to three miles (1 to 5 km) across to take advantage of a rich prey base of ancient murrelets, a seabird.

Still, this close nesting is not as dense as in the Snake River Birds of Prey Area. The Snake River is a deep chasm carved in the Idaho desert by the cataclysmic breaking of the natural dam of Bonneville Lake some 15,000 to 30,000 years ago. The steep red walls of the canyon are a sponge-like strata of cracks, fissures, and gas bubbles in ancient basalt. Over the 80 miles (130 km) of the Birds of Prey Area, as many as 200 pairs of breeding falcons perch in the canyon's natural pockets as close as 75 yards (80 m) from each other or an average of 712 yards (647 m) apart. During their breeding season, prairie falcons consume about 60,000 Townsend's ground squirrels that burrow in the soft soils around the canyon. But even this density is not as great as that of Paximada or the Isles of Mogador.

The surface of Paximada consists of loosely piled large and small rocks; the falcons nest in the crevices and holes among them. The Isles of Mogador are likewise a mosaic of crevices, potholes, and pigeonholes. The enormous prey base of small migrant birds that cross the Mediterranean Sea in late summer and fall account for the large density of Eleonora's falcons nesting in the area. On Paximada the distance between nest sites varies from 20 to 170 feet (6 to 50 m) but averages 65 to 100 feet (20 to 30 m). On Mogador the falcons nest even closer, with a range of from 3 to 50 feet (1 to 15 m) or an average of 30 feet (10 m).

The relatively dense falcon populations on the Queen Charlotte Islands, Snake River Canyon, and Paximada and Mogador provide

The Birds of Prey Area, farther along the Snake River in Idaho, is the breeding ground for more than 200 pairs of peregrines.

biologists with the opportunity to observe more than one pair at a time, which is why we know more about the falcons in these areas than we do of falcons at less populous sites. "With many of the solitary hawks and falcons you can sit around for hours and nothing happens. But at the nesting grounds of Eleonora's falcon, it is like a lively street café with something always going on," said biologist Hartmut Walter when he explained why he chose Paximada and Mogador as sites for his studies.

NESTING SITES

Though male falcons may pick the general nesting area, it is the female who determines the exact site where she will lay her eggs. With the exception of Australia's gray falcon, which has been reported to build nests on occasion, falcons aren't nest builders. About the only effort a falcon will make toward building a nest is to make a shallow scrape in loose soil or gravel, or perhaps to appropriate and line another bird's nest.

Peregrines, prairies — indeed, many falcons — prefer a ledge or hole on the sheer face of a rocky cliff or crag. The height provides safety from nest predators and gives the falcon a commanding perch from which to hunt. Tree holes or hollows are occasionally used, especially in areas with no suitable cliffs, such as Poland, northern Germany, and the eastern coast of the Baltic Sea.

Other falcon species prefer to steal their nests. Merlins like the stick nests of crows and magpies. Eurasian hobbies like crows' nests, too, though they'll take one from a gray heron, a black kite, or even a red squirrel. Sakers, which nest from eastern Europe to Mongolia, have been known to drive eagles away from their nests and then take over.

In England, Spain, and other European countries, falcons sometimes nest in man-made structures such as castles, churches, windmills, barns, bridges, and even city skyscrapers.

Falcons don't make their own nests like other birds, but use a shallow scrape on a ledge. Some falcons, like this merlin, may use an abandoned stick nest of another bird.

JAMES RICHARDS

COURTSHIP

During spring, the skies above the Queen Charlotte Islands are filled with the spectacle of peregrine courtship. In these aerial dances, the male is generally the more exuberant of the pair. "A typical courtship flight," said biologist Wayne Nelson, "may include a female lazily cruising along the cliff with the male putting on a power flight demonstration above her, flying with deep pumping wing beats, steeply diving, climbing, and turning while twisting his body so that light is reflected off his belly and underwing." The male may feign attacks on his mate, she turning over to display her talons, the pair sometimes locking talons for a moment, even touching beaks for an aerial kiss.

Sometimes courtship can take on a more ballet-like form. I saw two bat falcons in a courtship flight over the jungles of Guatemala. The male, which had perched atop a Mayan temple ruin before dawn, started calling to his mate after sunrise with a *ke-ke-ke-ke*. She answered him from the jungle with a food-begging call and then flew in to join him atop his temple perch. After a series of calls to each other they left the temple to perform their courtship ritual over the jungle. Both flew in enormous loops and figure eights, passed each other in midflight, and touched wings. The male stooped sharply into the jungle, then flew up to continue his dance with his mate.

The male's aerial displays and dives may be his way of showing off his hunting prowess, which is important in attracting the female because, once she has laid her eggs and until her chicks are big enough so that they no longer need to be brooded, she will have to depend on the male to provide all the food. In the final stages of courtship he will bring her most or all of the food she needs as evidence of his hunting skill. Presenting food is an integral part of the courtship of most falcon species.

On the islands of Paximada and Mogador where Eleonora's falcons nest, the breeding season is so precisely timed to the fall migration of prey birds that, when courtship begins, migratory birds are not yet available for prey and so the male lays dragonflies or other insect morsels at the female's feet, using them as love bait. Lesser kestrel males of Eurasia do the reverse. During courtship they offer their mates small mammals, birds, and lizards, though when the eggs hatch and the real job begins, more than 90 percent of what they bring home is insects.

The Isles of Mogador are a mosaic of crevices and potholes where large numbers of Eleonora's falcons gather to nest.

HARTMUT WALTER

The Eleonora's falcon performs the final stage of courtship much like the peregrine. The male bows rhythmically to his mate to initiate copulation. These bows last less than a second and are sometimes repeated more than a hundred times a minute. Only when the female assumes a horizontal position, loosening her tail feathers, sometimes calling with her beak wide open, does the male approach for mating. He flies to or jumps gently on her back, loosely balling his talons up to avoid hurting her. He balances there with fluttering wings. She shifts her tail to one side and he depresses his tail downward between her tail and wing to achieve sexual contact. Each copulation lasts between eight and twelve seconds, and the pair may copulate five or six times a day. This is about the same frequency as peregrines, though other species, such as European kestrels, can be a little more exuberant, copulating every few minutes, or up to seven times an hour. Falcons tend to make loud calls during the mating ritual, and on calm mornings they can be heard half a mile (a kilometer) away, advertising the existence of a successfully bonded pair on the territory.

Generally speaking, falcon pairs remain faithful to each other throughout the breeding season; with Eleonora's falcon that pair bond may last two seasons or more. However, fidelity seems tied

WAYNE NELSON

The male falcon bows rhythmically, sometimes more than a hundred times a minute, to the female to initiate copulation.

more to the site than to the mate, with males and females usually returning to the same place they bred last year, sometimes finding the same mate, sometimes discovering that the winter has taken last year's mate and they must find another. In Saskatoon, Saskatchewan, however, more than 68 percent of the urban-nesting merlins that survive from one year to the next switch mates.

Infidelity within a breeding season isn't unheard of, though. Mike Kochert, of the Bureau of Land Management's Raptor Research Project in the Snake River, saw one male "having an extramarital relationship right there in front of the whole canyon," but this is not usual. American kestrel females may wander among two or three territorial males in the early part of the breeding season, mating rather promiscuously before eventually settling down monogamously with one male.

THE EGGS

Females lay two to six eggs, depending on species, one every two to three days. The speckled brown and red eggs are large compared with those of most other birds — each egg is 5 to 10 percent of the female's body weight. The female does most of the incubating,

FRED BRUEMMER

The speckled brown and red eggs of the peregrine are large compared with those of most other birds — each egg weighing 5 to 10 percent of the female's body weight.

though males do help on occasion. Some males have more of a maternal instinct than others, and the female may even resort to sitting on the male to get him to abandon the eggs. For the most part, the male is kept from the nest by an exuberant female who constantly takes his food away and may even attack him if he sits too long. This rough treatment activates his aggressive behavior, which he then turns on the local prey to help keep dinner on the table for his growing family.

When an egg is ready to hatch, it develops a small crack or hole, and the chick slowly makes its entrance into the world, usually shedding its shell completely within twenty-four to forty-eight hours. On the first day, it is a helpless cotton ball, but, by the second day, it begins crawling about its nest, squawking and demanding food.

Feeding a brood of falcon chicks is evidently an exhausting job. In fact, on the Queen Charlottes, the number of nestlings raised in the preceding year is inversely proportional to the number of parents that are still alive the following year. Of the parent falcons that raise from zero to two youngsters, 77 percent survive to the following spring, but of the falcons that raise three or four youngsters, only 57 percent survive the harrowing winter.

On the Queen Charlotte Islands off the Pacific Coast of Canada, peregrine falcons move from the island rainforests in late winter to their palisade nesting sites that skirt the rocky island shores.

SIZE DIFFERENCE

In all falcon species, as with almost all other raptors, females have the size advantage. Female prairie, peregrine, and other large falcons can be from a quarter to a third larger than their mates.

Being larger, she is often able to get her way. If she wants a piece of meat, she takes it. If she wants to sit somewhere that he's sitting, he'd better move. Tom Cade, in his book *The Falcons of the World*, states that nature provides these birds with such "lethal weapons and fierce aggressive dispositions" that perhaps female dominance may be one way of keeping two evenly matched falcons from harming each other during mating and parenting.

Another hypothesis about the size difference suggests that males and females split up the food supply, so that they will not compete with each other. Since the male is smaller than the female he will naturally go after smaller prey than she. Thus, when the female finishes incubating the eggs and joins in the hunt to feed the growing brood, she will also naturally go after larger prey that is perhaps not so over-hunted. Although falcons normally pursue prey appropriate to their size, in a pinch they can take on all sizes. For falcons that prey on insects or relatively small birds or mammals, this explanation for size difference does not seem to apply.

There is also the "big mother" hypothesis. Bigger mothers are better mothers because they produce larger eggs, which lead to larger chicks, which have a better chance at survival. Also, a bigger mother is a warmer mother, less sensitive to the cold, able to hatch her eggs earlier in the season, and able to live off her own fat reserves during that busy period. However, in many other bird species, the opposite is true — females are smaller than males — so it is not certain that this is the reason for larger females in most birds of prey.

Argument persists over whether the female is dominant because she is larger. Wayne Nelson believes that although the female's larger size enables her to defend her nest better against large intruders and potential nest predators, "if you fight on the ground, there is an advantage to being bigger, but if you fight in the air, there is an advantage to being smaller." The male is the primary territory defender and his smaller size gives him more agility in aerial combat when he defends his territory or protects his prey from other male falcons or predators.

The Defense

Falcons defend their territories rigorously. Males do not tolerate other raptors or falcons or even neighboring young on their territory. Adults will readily adopt a flightless chick but will not tolerate fledgling intruders. At the Snake River Birds of Prey Area, biologist Mike Kochert observed an adult prairie falcon confront some human visitors who were walking along the canyon rim. In all the confusion, a neighboring, recently fledged falcon chick was flushed off the canyon wall and entered the adult prairie's territory. The adult immediately turned and stooped on the young bird and hit it. "It was dead before it hit the ground," says Kochert.

The falcons' territories are inviolate, even the smaller areas that Eleonora's falcons claim as their own. Hartmut Walter describes their territories in the Mediterranean as small "apartments" that are not trespassed upon by falcon neighbors. Here a falcon enters his property through flight corridors that seldom require trespass in another's air space.

Adult prairie falcons do not tolerate other raptors or falcons, or even neighboring young, on their nesting territory. Though they may readily adopt a flightless chick, they are capable of killing one who has taken to wing and invaded their territory.

The western red-footed falcon, which breeds from northeastern Europe through Russia and into Siberia, is perhaps the only falcon that tolerates the close presence of other falcons. During the breeding season adults gather together and put on territorial displays in flocks, soaring over their colonies or flying together in wave-like motions over the trees, twisting, flashing, and calling in unison.

Laggars, which nest in trees in southeast Asia, have been known to allow potential prey such as doves, rollers, and pigeons to share a tree — perhaps joining in a common vigilance for nest predators.

Falcons, however, have little patience with other raptors. On Padre Island, Texas, I once saw a peregrine falcon, which had taken up residence atop a tall condominium on the southern, developed side of the island, assault an osprey twice its size, which was attempting to share the falcon's perch. The falcon attacked in a series of dives while screaming — the osprey defended itself by inverting at the last instant, providing the smaller raptor with a bed of talons to land on, which the falcon somehow managed to avoid.

Biologists in the Snake River have observed prairie falcons kill trespassing great horned and barn owls. In one case Mike Kochert watched eight falcons descend on a golden eagle that flew through the canyon. "Prairie falcons hate golden eagles," says Kochert.

At Paximada, when eagles, hawks, herons, and other falcon species enter the air space around the island, as many as fifty to eighty Eleonora's falcons may scramble off the cliff, climb high into the sky, and dive-bomb the intruder until it is driven away.

A month or two after learning how to fly, many falcon species must be ready to join their parents on migrations that can be as long as 5,000 miles (8000 km).

CRAIG FLATTEN

In aerial attacks on other raptors, as with prey, falcons attempt to gain the height advantage before stooping on the back of their antagonist and delivering a blow or raking the intruder with their back talons. Two male falcons may actually lock talons and fall tumbling through the air, usually separating before impact, though biologists have seen falcons carry their disputes all the way to the ground.

Falcons are no less patient with humans who approach their nests. Biologists with the Greenland Peregrine Falcon Survey, in the course of banding falcons, wear crash helmets while rappeling off cliffs, partly to protect themselves in the event of a fall and partly to shield their heads from the attacks of adults. Most falcons will not strike a human intruder, but in the rare instances when they do, the result can be serious.

LEARNING TO FLY

Falcon aggression takes place in the nest as well. Falcon chicks are combative feeders, competing with their siblings for food. The youngest chick has less of a chance of surviving than its older sisters and brothers.

When really hungry, falcon chicks literally mob their parents when they enter the nest with food. Things can get even worse when they learn to fly, since the mob is no longer restrained by the nest and can take its attack out into midair. There is good reason then for the parents to try to keep their brood well fed.

On the Queen Charlotte Islands, Wayne Nelson watched an adult peregrine take an ancient murrelet before being ambushed by his own chicks. He'd just picked his prey up off the water when two of his youngsters came swooping in toward him. Heavily loaded and with little room to move, the male was forced to ditch his quarry into the water. All three then hovered over the spot where the murrelet disappeared, but the male soon went ashore. The murrelet later popped up behind them and swam to make its getaway. The father hadn't even had time to kill his catch. After several more tries, one fledgling grabbed the murrelet from the water, so the male's hunt and capture were not entirely for naught and may even have provided an important lesson for the young.

The young are awkward fliers when they first take to the air. Whereas adult birds are stable when they soar, the very young shift

Young gyrfalcons on the nest. Their first flights will be awkward, like a child learning to ride a bike.

constantly, trying to keep their balance, much like a child learning to ride a bicycle. During their first few days of flying, their landings often look like crash landings.

Parents don't wean their young, as other species do. Three to five weeks after fledging, the birds are sufficiently adept at capturing prey and cease to rely on their parents. Fledglings' first stoops at prey are awkward and inaccurate. Siblings may remain in loose hunting parties after they have left their parents. Still they are no match for older birds, which take advantage of their naiveté. At Point Reyes I watched two fledglings feeding when a two-year-old bird came in and stole their food. The two young birds, with down still sticking out of their collars, just stared in awe as the sleeker bird spread his stiff wings over the pirated meal and ate unchallenged.

In the Mediterranean, where the nesting season of Eleonora's falcons is timed with the fall migration of smaller European birds, the young are hatched much later, somewhere between late August and early September, so that most of their growth occurs as the migrating birds begin to cross the Mediterranean. Most of the young falcons' growth is completed after thirty to thirty-five days, with the growth period peaking between the tenth and fifteenth day, during which the chicks may gain up to three-quarters of an ounce (25 g) per day.

The chicks become increasingly noisy as they continue to grow, and the female responds to that natural pressure by joining the male in hunting for the brood. The chicks put on an enormous amount of fatty tissue and may weigh more than their parents in the end. This fatty tissue is vital, for soon the young falcons must learn to hunt for themselves and those fat reserves will help them survive when they are still inexperienced in capturing prey. Still, as many as 50 percent of the young will not survive their first year.

Life is hard for a first-year falcon. A month or two after learning how to fly, many species must be ready to undertake long migrations. Eleonora's falcons don't have the luxury of even that much time. From fifteen to twenty-six days after they first test their wings, the fall migration of Europe's songbirds winds down, and the young falcons must be ready to join their parents on their own long journey, traveling more than 3,500 miles (5500 km) to wintering grounds in Madagascar.

KEN STRAITON/FIRST LIGHT

In the Greek islands the young are hatched in late August and early September (much later than other species) to take advantage of the abundant food supply provided by the fall migration of smaller European songbirds.

Females lay two to six eggs, depending on species, one every two to three days. These are in a merlin's nest.

EDGAR JONES

The female merlin sits on the eggs while the male is out hunting for the whole family.

JAMES RICHARDS

JAMES RICHARDS

A merlin and her brood. The job of feeding growing young falcons is exhausting. It can even affect an adult falcon's ability to survive the following winter.

FRED BRUEMMER

On the first day, a falcon chick is a helpless cotton ball, but it grows rapidly, squawking and demanding food.

ANTHONY MERCIECA/PHOTO RESEARCHERS

Sibling peregrine falcons may remain in loose hunting parties after they have left their parents, but they soon must learn to hunt by themselves.

PAT & TOM LEESON/PHOTO RESEARCHERS

All falcon chicks, including these prairie falcons, are combative feeders, competing with their siblings for food. The youngest chick has less chance of surviving than its older sisters and brothers.

NICO MYBURGH

Above:
A white-eyed kestrel feeds her young.
Falcons time their nesting and breeding
seasons to the arrival of spring or the
local availability of prey.

Right:
This white-eyed kestrel has taken over
another bird's abandoned nest.

Opposite:
Here a kestrel incubates her eggs.
Though males may pick the general
nesting area, it is the female who
will determine the exact site where
she will lay.

NICO MYBURGH

4
THE LONG JOURNEY

FALCON MIGRATIONS EVOLVED MILLIONS OF YEARS AGO, PERHAPS AS falcon ancestors began to leave the equatorial jungles to test out their newly acquired aerial hunting abilities on the open grasslands and savannahs. A few more adventurous falcons began to explore areas farther north and south for seasonal blooms of insects, mammals, and birds to satisfy the food demands of the breeding season. When the breeding season was over some stayed, but others returned and thus perhaps took the first migrations.

Not all falcons migrate. Of the thirty-eight species, twenty-four are nonmigratory. The others migrate twice a year. Species that nest in subtropical or tropical latitudes are normally resident year-round, though they may disperse locally at the end of the nesting season or with the local variability of prey. Island inhabitants tend to follow this same trend. Thus falcons in Britain are nonmigratory, though Eurasian arctic species move south into Europe, Africa, the Middle East, China, and southeast Asia. The six species of falcons in Australia are also nonmigratory.

Up to 90 percent of all Canada's falcons migrate south, taking the first good north wind that comes down from the Arctic in early fall. According to biologist Richard Fyfe, formerly with the Canada Wildlife Service, "there is a tendency for the most northern falcons to migrate farthest south. Among falcon biologists it is known as 'leap frogging.'"

Peregrines are such leap froggers, some individuals traveling all the way from above the Arctic Circle to southern South America. Unlike the gyrfalcon, which is better adapted to the cold and can survive on such winter prey species as the ptarmigan and the arctic

"Peregrine" means wanderer or migrator, and the peregrine falcon is the most migratory of all the falcons.

hare, the peregrine must follow the songbirds, shorebirds, and water-fowl south. What it loses in time spent traveling it gains in greater availability of prey and longer daylight hours to catch that prey.

"Peregrine" means wanderer or migrator, and the peregrine falcon is the most migratory of all falcons. It is also more susceptible than other falcons to poisons in our environment, and since it migrates through every continent except Antarctica, its migrations have been followed more closely than that of any other species.

Prairie falcons also migrate, though not nearly as far as the peregrine. When their ground squirrel prey stay underground to avoid

FRED BRUEMMER

Because it is the most migratory, the peregrine is more susceptible than other falcons to poisons in our environment, and thus its migrations have been followed more closely.

Though some merlins remain behind on the breeding grounds, many undertake long migrations.

the mid-summer heat, the Snake River's prairies may travel as far north as southern Canada and then in fall winter as far south as Sonora, Mexico.

The peregrines on the Queen Charlotte Islands are one of the few Canadian peregrine populations in which the adults do not migrate. The prey base of ancient murrelets and other small seabirds is sufficient year-round to keep the adults there, though many of the juvenile birds disperse south along the Pacific coast of southern British Columbia and the United States where winter is a little less harsh.

The Queen Charlottes' peregrines pay a high price for their winter stay, however — they have an average annual mortality rate of 31.5 percent compared with 10 to 25 percent for adult peregrines in other populations in milder climates. Perhaps the greatest cause of death on the Queen Charlottes is the arctic cold fronts that blow down from the Bering Sea. "Two weeks of bad weather means you can't hunt, and if you don't have enough fat reserves, you are going to starve," says Wayne Nelson.

Though some merlins remain behind on the breeding grounds, many undertake long migrations. In North America, merlins migrate south to spend their winters all the way from southern Canada to northwestern South America, with a few traveling across the equator to northern Peru. In the Old World merlins travel from Iceland to the north coast of Africa, from Europe to the Mediterranean, and from Siberia and Manchuria into southeastern China and even Vietnam. In general, Eurasian merlins don't go as far south as their North American cousins, perhaps because of competition in Africa, where there are more falcon species than anywhere else in the world.

Old World kestrels nesting in the Eurasian Arctic spend their winters in Africa, China, and the Middle East, though most of the kestrels in the United Kingdom stay there all year. The relatively mild winter and year-round food supplies of the British Isles give its residential falcons little need to fly south.

Hobbies that breed throughout Europe and Asia are highly migratory and travel south to southern China, Burma, the Indian subcontinent, and into Africa from Kenya on south. There in southern Africa they are joined by eastern red-footed falcons, which arrive from breeding grounds in Siberia, Mongolia, Manchuria, Korea, and northern China.

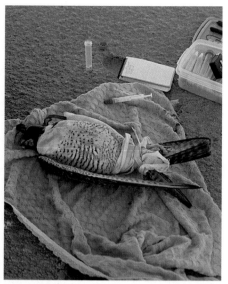

GARY BORTOLOTTI   GARY BORTOLOTTI   A. PALLERONI

STUDIES

The migrations of raptors in general (eagles, hawks, and falcons) are studied at a number of places in North America, including the Goshute Mountains in Nevada in the United States, the coast of Vera Cruz in Mexico, and Point Pelee on Lake Ontario in Canada. Most migration study spots lie along coastlines or long ridgelines that funnel these raptors through in heavy concentrations. Only at Assateague Island in Maryland, Cape May in New Jersey, and Padre Island in Texas, are there sufficient concentrations of falcons for falcons-only banding stations.

Migrating raptors are also studied in Europe at a banding station on the Island of Helgoland, off Germany in the North Sea. England and Scotland have extensive banding programs, though the United Kingdom's falcons are nonmigratory. Still, for the most part, falcon migration banding stations are a North American phenomenon. At most migration stations in Europe and the Middle East, the birds are simply counted in order to spot any decline in particular species. Most of the in-depth studies are done on the breeding grounds.

Migrating raptors, including falcons, are observed at the Straits of Bosporus, which connect the Black Sea and the Sea of Marmara near Istanbul, a migration point for many raptors. Biologists make the pilgrimage there each fall.

Egyptian ornithologists run a raptor banding station on the Egyptian side of the Gulf of Suez. But in the Middle East perhaps one of

Left and center:
An American kestrel is drawn to a trap loaded with one of its favorite meals, then carefully weighed and measured.

Above:
This peregrine is being banded. DNA fingerprinting may someday replace banding, telling biologists exactly where these falcons are from.

the Old World's most productive migration routes is at Eilat, Israel, where biologists counted more than three-quarters of a million raptors during the spring of 1977. For the past five years, biologists under the sponsorship of the Israeli Raptor Information Center have been banding raptors at Eilat, including peregrines, kestrels, hobbies, and barbary falcons.

The most frequently banded are barbary falcons, which are residents rather than migrants. They breed along the Mediterranean coast of North Africa into Israel, Saudi Arabia, and possibly Iraq. Here the barbary falcon replaces the peregrine, though some argue that the barbary falcon is in fact another race of peregrine.

Champion Fliers

Most raptors prefer to travel along coastlines rather than to strike out across a very large body of water. Most migrating raptors often rely on ridgelines because they can ride the thermal updrafts. Falcons and other raptors use these updrafts to circle to high altitudes and then glide down to the next thermal. Still, falcons by nature of their narrow wings and heavier wing loading are not as dependent on thermals as hawks and eagles are.

Bill Cochran, a scientist with the Center for Wildlife Ecology in Champagne, Illinois, has been following radio-tagged migrating falcons in spotter planes since 1973. He discovered that merlins would begin their flight an hour (peregrines about twenty minutes)

Barbary falcons are residents rather than migrants, remaining on their breeding grounds along the Mediterranean coast of North Africa into Israel, Saudi Arabia, and possibly Iraq, all year round.

A.E. SIRULNIKOFF/FIRST LIGHT

before sunrise and would fly low and direct as far as 70 miles (110 km) before encountering thermals. Though the falcons averaged 110 miles (175 km) a day, there are exceptions. Cochran once followed a migrating peregrine falcon that flew nonstop over the ocean all the way from Assateague, Maryland, to Cuba, a distance of 1,000 miles (1600 km) in only forty-eight hours.

Eleonora's falcons migrate all the way from the Mediterranean Sea to Madagascar, but are seldom seen on the migration route. Biologist Hartmut Walter believes the birds may fly this route at altitudes so high that they pass unnoticed from below. Along Padre Island, where the humidity filled the air, I found that falcons disappeared rapidly into the sky. Usually thermals rise from 2,000 to 3,000

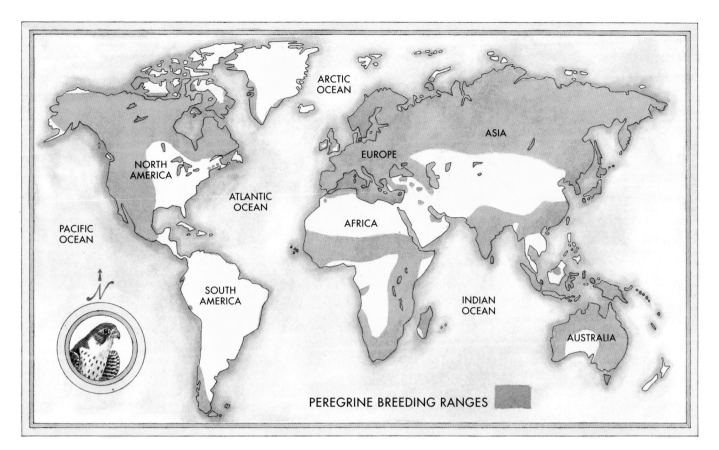

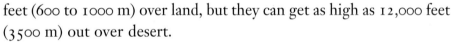

PEREGRINE BREEDING RANGES

Eleonora's falcons migrate all the way from the Mediterranean Sea to Madagascar, but are seldom seen on the migration route. They may travel too high to be sighted from below.

feet (600 to 1000 m) over land, but they can get as high as 12,000 feet (3500 m) out over desert.

Since 1988, Bud Anderson, who is with the Falcon Research Group in Bow, Washington, and biologist Oscar Beingolea from Lima, Peru, have been studying migratory peregrine falcons after they land in Chile, Argentina, Peru, and Ecuador. They have so far sighted a number of birds that were first banded in Greenland, Padre Island, and Cape May. They are also finding a number of peregrines that arrive in South America in pairs and are trying to find out if these wintering pairs stay together when they return to their nesting grounds in summer.

Anderson feels, however, that calling these falcons "wintering" birds is inaccurate. "These birds nest in the Arctic during a time of twenty-four hours of light and then follow that light south. These birds know no winter." The falcons also spend more time in South America than they do in North America, and Anderson and Beingolea conjecture that it would be more proper to call these birds South American residents that travel north only for the nesting season.

Anderson and Beingolea hope to find out more about "wintering" peregrines. For the most part these falcons breed in the Arctic, where human populations are still sparse, but they spend the rest of the year in some of the most densely populated areas on earth where the jungle is rapidly disappearing. The continuing demands upon native habitat could be disastrous. Biologists need to know what areas are critical to these migrating falcons and their prey species.

MECCA FOR FALCONS

The huge off-road tires of our three-wheel all-terrain vehicles (ATVs) charge through the loose sand along the inland shore of South Padre Island, off Texas, in the Gulf of Mexico. I am following Alberto Palleroni, a biologist with the Padre Island Peregrine Falcon Survey, looking for migrant peregrines.

Peregrines begin their southbound journeys when the songbirds, shorebirds, and waterfowl, which the peregrines feed on, move south for the winter. The falcons stop off at Padre Island on their long journey from their nesting grounds in Canada and Greenland to their wintering grounds in Central or South America. More peregrines are banded here than at any other place in the world. Though kestrels and merlins also migrate through Padre, the peregrines are singled out for

PETER GINN

Peregrine falcons that migrate to South America gain a greater availability of prey and longer daylight hours to catch them.

their endangered species status, and as they are more sensitive to pesticides, their decline is more likely to signal problems in the environment. And since peregrine falcons migrate all the way from northern Canada to Argentina and from the Russian Arctic to South Africa, they serve as environmental barometers for virtually the entire world.

I'm not used to the ATV yet. Its vibration and speed — we're going about highway speed — both scare and exhilarate me. Though it is late afternoon in mid-October, the air off the Gulf is warm and humid.

Now Palleroni slows his vehicle to a stop, and I catch up. He scans the horizon with his binoculars. "There's one!" he yells over the sound of the motors.

I try to orient my binoculars in the direction he's looking but see only specks on the horizon. "Where?" I ask.

Alberto takes some pains to point it out. Finally I see that one of the specks is a falcon, its silhouette wavering in the mirage that the sun draws up off the sand. It is my first day on the island. Eventually my eyes adjust and I, too, begin to pick out the specks that are falcons, though never as efficiently as Palleroni.

Padre Island, Texas, is a stop-off for migrating peregrine falcons that feed there on the rich prey base of migrant and shore birds.

A. PALLERONI

The falcon is on the inland edge of the island, where the sand mixes with the water in a sandy mud that even the ATVs can't negotiate. We make an attempt to charge through the mud, but when our motors begin to die, we turn back.

We continue along the shore. Abruptly our fast-moving vehicles flush a dove from a clump of low brush. As the dove rises into the haze above us, suddenly a peregrine falcon stoops down directly at the dove. The dove dodges the falcon and barely escapes with its life. At the bottom of its dive, the falcon swoops back up above the dove, dives again, still misses but tries again. On the fourth stoop feathers fly as the dove is buffeted to the ground.

Palleroni rushes to the kill, chasing the falcon off before it has had a chance to carry away its quarry. The biologist sets a trap over the prey with a radio-controlled net. We back off and watch the action through binoculars.

At first the falcon is leery. It approaches its kill cautiously, flies a little closer, finally takes the bait — and then the trap is sprung.

We hop back on our bikes and rush out to where the falcon struggles with the net. Palleroni cautiously handles the bird. No bird has ever been injured in this study, and the biologist doesn't want this to be the first one. He places a hood over the falcon's head to calm it down.

The falcon is a female. The thick vertical bars on her underside reveal that she is also a juvenile. "A haggard" — an older bird — "wouldn't have missed like that," declares Palleroni. "That's one of the reasons so many falcons don't make it through their first migration. It takes practice to become a truly efficient hunter."

I ask Palleroni if he had seen that falcon before it began its attack. He admits he didn't, that many of the birds on Padre Island circle up so high you can't see them. "But they're there. Just the other day I flushed up a bird and seven falcons dropped out of the sky. They all took turns chasing it until one of them nailed it. Then the rest of the falcons just rose up into the ozone and disappeared."

From his field kit, Palleroni takes a syringe and extracts a sample of blood from the bird. Then he bands the bird and sprays her neck with a yellow dye. The dye will last only a few weeks but will let the survey biologists know that this is a bird they've already looked at.

Palleroni removes the hood from the proud falcon, who remains wide-eyed but regal, a little angry but unafraid. The biologist tosses the bird into the air. The falcon spreads her wings but flies off unhurried.

WAYNE NELSON

Queen Charlotte Islands' peregrines remain here all year, but pay a high price for their winter's stay — higher than average mortality rates.

About 50 feet (15 m) out she turns right and starts circling us. "She's trying to figure out what that was all about," said Palleroni.

Then the bird rises and disappears into the haze above us.

We continue our hunt. During peak days, it isn't unusual to encounter as many as thirty falcons on Padre Island. This year's survey biologists will follow the migration throughout October, and they will band some 300 birds.

In the spring of 1990, 36 percent of the birds captured had already been banded, most on Padre Island. "That's telling us that they are taking the same route each year," said falcon biologist Tom Maechtle, the survey's field operations manager. Among the 1990 banded birds were a number that had come from Greenland, Canada, Argentina, Ecuador, and other places in North and South America. These findings are helping the survey's biologists piece together a picture of a migration that can take these birds a distance greater than 5,000 miles (8000 km), one of the longest migrations of any animal on earth.

Palleroni also works with the Greenland Peregrine Falcon Survey. Several of the Greenland survey's banded birds have also shown up on Padre Island. The team studies the fall and the spring migrations.

The project has its roots in the 1960s and 1970s when various groups, including Texas Parks and Wildlife, began banding falcons. It was not until 1978 that the group obtained its grant from the U.S. Fish and Wildlife Service, and the survey went beyond just banding to monitoring annual peregrine populations, collecting genetic information, and gathering general data on diet, mortality, and toxic residues.

Padre Island is an important stop-off for peregrine falcons on their long migrations. Many birds migrate from northern tundra, and Padre looks a lot like barren tundra to a falcon. It is a long, narrow island of treeless sand that stretches down the southeast Texas coast for more than a hundred miles.

On the Gulf side are beaches and vegetated dunes, but on the inland side are wide sandy flats, which fluctuate with a tide that leaves tiny crabs and crustaceans for the smaller birds to feed upon. The tides also foster dark algal mats that cover much of the flats, supporting the insect community that in turn supports the falcons' prey. Peregrines prefer to hunt over open expanses, and the broad sandy flats and dunes on Padre provide little area for prey to escape.

Falcons that migrate down the North American continent use Padre as a resting point. There they hunt and put on some needed fat reserves to complete their arduous journey. Some birds have stayed as long as a month on Padre in either fall or spring. The Gulf coast is in fact the only known spring staging ground of peregrines in the western hemisphere.

Scientists hope to learn more about the falcons' migratory routes by banding them at breeding, migrating, and wintering points. It's necessary to know all these locations if the scientists are going to be able to pinpoint exactly where birds are affected by toxins or deforestation, but banding is a laborious process. To get reports back on 100 falcons, biologists have to band 10,000, since the odds of recapturing a banded bird are 100 to 1.

Padre Island Peregrine Falcon Survey biologists are excited about some new methods of DNA analysis — DNA "fingerprinting" — in which biologists can read a falcon's DNA signature in its blood. With these methods biologists will be able to identify different populations of birds and where they come from, even without the benefit of bands.

At twilight, we return to the survey's headquarters on the island, and I watch as Palleroni takes the blood samples from the day's trapping and turns them over to Connie Oar, who's in charge of the survey's logistics as well as handling and cataloging the blood samples.

Since the beginning, the Padre Island Falcon Survey has been collecting two cubic centimeters of blood from each of the captured birds. One-tenth of that goes to Don Morizot, the head of the project, who is conducting the DNA analysis. Morizot tries to locate the birthplace of each falcon by comparing the results of the analysis with samples from known origins in Canada, Alaska, and Greenland. The rest of the samples will be sent to biologist Wally Jarmen in Santa Cruz, California, for pesticide analysis. Jarmen has also done vitamin analysis of wild-caught falcons to determine normal vitamin levels. This has helped biologists with captive breeding populations whose offspring are being used to restock the wild.

The survey headquarters is a beach house on the edge of a development on South Padre Island. The island is a popular vacation spot for tourists who come here, especially in the winter, looking for sun, sand, and sea. Just north of the city's development boundaries are the open dunes, tidal flats, and algal mats. Maechtle worries that development will spread and carve up these vital falcon resources:

A peregrine falcon closes in on a mallard. Falcons must take advantage of prey species along the way if they are to survive the journey.

A. PALLERONI

FRED BRUEMMER

"I am particularly concerned about the tidal flats and algal mats. People look at these and think it is a waste, yet it is a really rich biosystem. This is a key area for the peregrine falcons. If they develop this area they are going to upset the normal flow of the migration."

The Padre Island Falcon Survey spots some 1,500 to 2,000 birds each season; many more pass through without getting spotted. World peregrine population estimates vary between 12,000 and 18,000 breeding pairs. When nonbreeding adults and juveniles are included, the total world population in the fall may be 22,000 to 108,000 peregrines. If two or three falcons are missed for every one that is sighted, perhaps an estimated 5,000 birds pass Padre Island each fall, which means Padre may actually be the stopping point for approximately 5 percent of the world's peregrines.

Over the course of the project, a number of birds have been captured repeatedly. Padre Island biologists hope that by studying these birds, determining where they come from and where they go at different times in their lives, they will get a better idea of the birds' biology, of the problems encountered over the falcons' vast range, and how these problems affect them over their entire life span.

The gyrfalcon makes its home in the Arctic where its favorite food is the ptarmigan.

The white-eyed kestrel hunts the dry grasslands and scrub of Africa, taking insects, lizards, small mammals, and even some small snakes off the ground.

A close relative of the Old World kestrel, the Australian kestrel also hunts from its perch or while hovering in the wind.

W.S. CLARK

The barbary falcon, also known as the red-naped or black shaheen, breeds in the desert and arid scrub of North Africa and the Middle East where it preys on birds, which it takes in the air.

5
THE POISONED EGG

FALCONS LIVE AT THE TOP OF THE FOOD CHAIN AND ARE SUBJECT TO what biologists call biomagnification of pesticides. Animals that ingest persistent pesticides such as DDT and its breakdown product DDE don't digest them quite like other substances; instead the poisons accumulate in the fat cells. The insect that eats the plant gets one dose of poison, and the bird that eats the insect gets an even greater dose because the poison has already biomagnified within the insect, but the falcon that eats the bird gets the greatest dose of all.

It was in the 1950s and 1960s that the decline of one such predator, the peregrine falcon, alerted the world to the damage DDT and other organochlorine pesticides were having on the environment. Peregrines were affected more than other falcons because they migrated more and because they ate birds almost exclusively. No other falcon populations were as severely affected.

In 1962, at the 12th International Ornithological Congress at Cornell University in Ithaca, New York, Joseph Hickey, a falcon expert, heard the rumor that no falcon had fledged that year in southeastern Canada or the northeastern United States. Hickey, who was with the Department of Wildlife Ecology at the University of Wisconsin, discounted it at first, but when later that year Derek Ratcliffe of the United Kingdom's Nature Conservancy Council published his paper "The Status of the Peregrine in Great Britain," Hickey began to sense the impending tragedy.

Ratcliffe was the first scientist to report what would become a worldwide problem. The bleak facts were that the peregrine falcon population in Great Britain, which before World War II numbered 820 pairs (one of the densest populations in the world), had plummeted to 378 pairs.

In 1964 biologists discovered that the peregrine was seriously endangered.

Hickey visited Ratcliffe in Scotland and was given a fast tour of the countryside and a number of historic nests. Hickey listened as Ratcliffe enumerated the grim statistics on vacant nests, egg breaking, failure of incubated eggs to hatch, death of chicks, small broods, failure to lay, and failure of birds to pair.

Hickey returned home in panic. From his files he pulled his extensive survey of the peregrine, which was undertaken in the 1930s, and pinpointed known peregrine nests on detailed maps. He then sent two researchers out to check locations in southeastern Canada and the northeastern United States. The survey team checked 133 locations toward the end of the 1964 peregrine nesting season. The results sent a shock wave through the North American ornithological community. The rumor had been correct — every single nest was deserted.

Hickey put out an alarm. In 1965 more than sixty ornithologists from all over Europe and North America gathered at Madison, Wisconsin, for the historic Madison Peregrine Conference to discuss the tragedy. Over several days biologists shared their thoughts, carrying their discussions on in hotel rooms late into the night.

Derek Ratcliffe and Ian Prestt of Great Britain, fresh from a NATO-sponsored symposium at Monks Wood on the toxic effects of persistent organochlorine pesticides on the environment, were the first to point their fingers at organochlorines. Parent falcons were breaking and eating their own eggs, something that had never been reported before, and Ratcliffe suspected that organochlorines might be the cause, though he had yet to discover the link. In 1948 G. Harper Hall, an amateur ornithologist, saw falcons eating their own eggs on Montreal's Sun Life building, but was so shocked that he didn't mention it in his initial account of the Sun Life's peregrines.

By the end of the conference, it became crystal clear to the biologists that accelerated adult mortalities and increased reproductive failures were taking a worldwide toll. In North America, which once supported 7,000 to 10,000 peregrine nesting sites, the results were grim. Only a third of all Rocky Mountain nests were now occupied. In Alaska and northern Canada, which historically supported the bulk of the falcon populations, the birds had declined by 55 to 65 percent. And east of the Mississippi, in the United States and in Canada south of the boreal forest, the peregrine was essentially eradicated. In Europe the toll was equally devastating. The peregrine in eastern and

DDT caused peregrines to lay eggs with shells so thin that they broke before hatching.

central Sweden, southeastern Norway, and southern Finland was almost extinct. In West Germany the raptor's population was a tenth of historic numbers.

The Culprit

Though the conference agreed that persistent organochlorine insecticides were the villains, exactly which pesticide was doing the damage was in dispute. In general Britons and a number of other Europeans thought that adult mortality was caused by the cyclodiene insecticides — aldrin, heptachlor, and especially dieldrin — which were used as seed dressings. Seed-eating birds that fed on the tainted food were loaded with enough pesticide to ultimately kill the peregrines that preyed on them. North Americans, however, believed DDT was the greater villain.

DDT's role was a little more insidious. It was introduced in the late 1940s and saw widespread use as a general insecticide on virtually all common crop species.

Again it was Ratcliffe who first hypothesized that insecticides caused decreased eggshell thickness, which resulted in females breaking the very eggs they were incubating. He compared a large sample

In the 1950s and 1960s the decline of the peregrine falcon alerted the world to the damage DDT and other organochlorine pesticides were having on the environment.

of eggshells from the British Museum with broken shells and found that the broken shells were lighter.

North American scientists confirmed Ratcliffe's results, going underground to check eggshell thickness by contacting egg collectors and weighing and measuring their then highly illegal caches of peregrine eggs.

The peregrine was perhaps the best known but not the only bird to be affected by the pesticides. Robins were reportedly dropping dead on the University of Michigan campus, while the brown pelican and the osprey were having the same problem as the peregrine with eggshell thinning and declining populations. Even the bald eagle was affected.

Not until pesticides were connected with cancer and began showing up in human mothers' milk did the world finally take action. In the Scandinavian countries DDT and the cyclodienes were banned by 1972, in West Germany by 1974, in Spain by 1977, and in Great

DDT-thinned peregrine eggshells from chicks hatched at the University of California at Santa Cruz Predatory Bird Research Lab.

Britain in successive voluntary restrictions from 1965 to 1975. In all the European Economic Community countries, any remaining uses of DDT and the cyclodienes were banned by 1983. In the United States they were banned by 1972, and in Canada by 1970.

However, the peregrine decline did not abate. The pesticides, though no longer sprayed on crops, lingered upon the land, in the streams, in the lakes, and in the ocean. In Finland, Norway, and Sweden, populations continued to fall in the early and mid-1970s to only 3 to 5 percent of pre–World War II levels. In the northern German plains, the extensive tree-nesting populations were extinct by 1972. In the Swiss Jura Mountains, only one breeding pair was left by 1971.

In the 1970 North American Peregrine Survey, only four pairs were found at eighty-two former nesting sites in southern Canada. Tom Cade of Cornell University and Richard Fyfe of the Canadian Wildlife Service predicted in a joint report that the species would be wiped out on the continent within the decade if the rate of decline did not abate, and the results of their 1975 survey showed that the decline continued. In all of North America that year only 324 nesting pairs of peregrines (out of historic figures of from 7,000 to 10,000) could be found. But the peregrine falcon finally turned the corner.

The Rebound

The first peregrine populations to rebound were in those areas where they had traditionally been the most numerous, such as Spain, Great Britain, and Australia. Populations around Victoria, Australia, had dropped by 30 percent, but further decline was arrested by controls placed on certain pesticides and by immigrants from healthy populations of peregrines elsewhere in the country that came in to fill the void.

In Great Britain, where restriction on pesticides began in 1962, the decline had actually stabilized by 1965. In a 1971 survey by the British Trust for Ornithology and the Nature Conservancy, the first evidence of "incipient" recovery appeared. Still, that recovery was largely restricted to the inland districts of Scotland and to a lesser degree northern England. The coastal districts, especially in southeast England, showed no recovery.

Most nations listed the peregrine falcon as a protected species by the mid-1970s. Where substantial populations remained, as in Britain and Australia, the falcons were able to rebuild their numbers by natural increase once the pesticide hazard abated. But where the peregrine populations were simply gone or at very low numbers, massive recovery efforts were put into gear.

Shortly after the 1965 Madison Peregrine Conference, a group of those who attended established the Raptor Research Foundation, an international group that fostered research and education regarding birds of prey through newsletters, conferences, and a scientific journal. RRF initially focussed on captive breeding, and its falconer members began establishing pairs of peregrines and other raptors in frantic efforts to discover techniques to reliably breed these high-strung birds in captivity. Captive breeding offered the hope for survival of the species. Many individuals — falconers, biologists, zookeepers, aviculturists, and bird fanciers — contributed. Newsletters, information exchanges, and conferences on captive breeding of birds of prey kept these people in the forefront of a desperate venture. Finally the pieces began to fall into place in the late 1960s and early 1970s with several widely scattered successful captive breedings of peregrines and other large raptors. Artificial insemination, artificial incubation, and a variety of other procedures were perfected. In less than ten years, a broad spectrum of motivated raptor enthusiasts in North America and Europe turned the wide-scale captive breeding of peregrines from a dream into a reality.

In West Germany, Christian Saar, a veterinarian from Hamburg, began a program of captive breeding and cross-fostering. By taking the first set of eggs, which the female would replace, and putting them into nests of foster parent Eurasian kestrels, northern goshawks, and common buzzards, Saar was able to get two families for the price of one.

In Sweden, Peter Lindberg, with the Swedish Society for Conservation of Nature, also began captive breeding. He kept falcons in outdoor aviaries to expose the birds to natural light and weather. Scandinavian peregrine eggshells were then the most contaminated in Europe, but Lindberg's program held out hope. Their first successful breeding took place in 1979 and their release in 1982.

In the Swiss Jura Mountains the first clutches of peregrine eggs were taken from wild nests, incubated in laboratories, and later returned to the nests, where peregrine parents put in extra time for these extended broods.

GALEN ROWELL/MOUNTAIN LIGHT PHOTOGRAPHY

A biologist replaces peregrine eggs with dummies while the real eggs are taken to the lab for highly controlled hatching.

In 1965 the peregrine in eastern and central Sweden, southeastern Norway, and southern Finland was almost extinct. In West Germany the falcons' population was a tenth of the historic numbers.

In Canada, where the 1970 survey results had been so bleak for the *anatum* peregrine (one of the three principal subspecies in North America), Richard Fyfe requested permission to take some birds into captivity at a meeting of federal and provincial wildlife directors in Yellowknife. In the absence of an official breeding facility, twelve immature peregrines were housed in a barn on Fyfe's acreage northeast of Edmonton until the Canadian Wildlife Service's facility could be built in Wainwright, Alberta.

Their first reproductive success occurred in 1972 with captive prairie falcons and was followed in 1974 by the first hatching of an *anatum* peregrine. In 1975 the first releases were attempted, and in 1977 a released captive-bred peregrine reproduced in the wild.

Fyfe had studied the peregrines' natural reproductive cycles and modeled all his indoor artificial incubation and captive-rearing techniques after the real thing. He also promoted international cooperation among falcon biologists. When the Peregrine Fund was getting started in the United States in 1973, there was a "hot line" between falcon breeding facilities in Canada and the U.S., according to Fyfe.

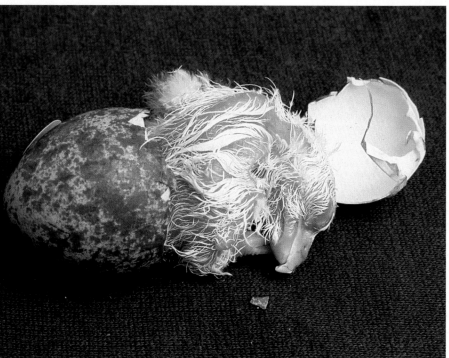

The recovery effort was launched in the United States when Tom Cade began a captive-breeding program of his own at Cornell University on a shoestring budget from the university and the National Science Foundation. When the lab of ornithology started receiving unsolicited checks from contributors, Cade opened a bank account, which he offhandedly labeled the Peregrine Fund. In 1974 his group incorporated under that name. To date the Peregrine Fund has released more than 3,000 captive-bred falcons, establishing more than 300 nesting pairs in the wild.

In 1985 more than 500 biologists gathered at the Sacramento Conference in Sacramento, California, to assess this worldwide effort twenty years after the historic Madison Conference, which had heralded the most sustained, successful, and expensive effort ever launched to save a wild animal.

As a result of captive releases, there were 63 documented nesting attempts and 128 young peregrine falcons produced in the eastern United States, where the species was earlier thought to have been eradicated. In Canada, 418 birds had been released to the wild, and birds had been sighted the following year at nearly every release site. In West Germany, 244 birds had been released, and in Sweden 82 birds.

Left:
A peregrine chick at its world debut. Each incubator has a heating element, monitored by two thermostats. The second is a backup that goes into effect if the temperature rises more than a quarter of a degree over its preset value.

Above:
A peregrine chick slowly emerges from its egg. During the next thirty-two to thirty-five days, the chick will balloon from about one ounce (28 g) to more than twenty ounces (567 g).

GALEN ROWELL/MOUNTAIN LIGHT PHOTOGRAPHY

JIM WEAVER/PEREGRINE FUND

Above:

Peregrine chicks are weighed and banded. In some wild areas banded birds raised in captivity and subsequently released account for 50 percent of the wild population.

Right:

A biologist feeds the young chicks "quail mush" — ground-up quail from the 120,000 Japanese coturnix quail that the World Center for Birds of Prey raises each year.

By 1985, persistent organochlorine pesticides were finally beginning to disappear from the environment with resultant increases in the numbers of peregrine falcons worldwide. In Great Britain the total population in the wild had increased to between 787 and 816 pairs, within 10 percent of historic levels.

In 1985 the population in West Germany was more than 130 breeding pairs, with 190 to 200 fledged young. Still, the tree-nesting population of the northern plains has not recovered, though efforts are being made to hack young peregrines in trees or give hatchlings to goshawk foster parents.

In the Swiss Jura Mountains the population had increased from one nesting pair in 1971 to more than fifty in 1985, with nearly a hundred pairs in all of Switzerland. In Europe the total peregrine population was at least 4,000 pairs. North America had at least 1,153 pairs. To date those numbers have continued to increase, and there is much talk in both the United States and Canada of removing the peregrine from the endangered species list.

To Hatch an Egg

At the World Center for Birds of Prey in Boise, Idaho, the current home of the Peregrine Fund, Cal Sandfort, the falcon propagation specialist for the Rocky Mountain Northwest Program, is standing with me in front of a bank of television screens that show the chambers of fifteen of the center's ninety pairs of falcons. Each chamber contains a camera and a microphone. Whenever any of the falcons vocalizes — as they would upon mating — a light goes on under one of the screens, alerting Sandfort so he can switch a monitor to that chamber.

According to Sandfort, his goal is to get the maximum number of eggs, the maximum fertility, and the maximum hatchability. Captive breeding on this scale has been possible only in the last twenty years. "This is accelerated production," he says. "It gives you a much higher rate of success than in the wild."

The first clutch of eggs is removed. Generally Sandfort will allow the falcon to incubate them for the first seven days. Apparently, there is something nature does in those seven days that can't be reproduced in the incubators, though a small chicken is sometimes introduced to serve as surrogate for the peregrine falcon's natural mother during the initial seven days.

Sandfort has sixteen incubators, which hold from twelve to fifteen eggs each. Each incubator has a heating element, monitored by two thermostats. The second thermostat is a backup that goes into effect

GALEN ROWELL/MOUNTAIN LIGHT PHOTOGRAPHY

Prairie falcon chicks in a cross-foster nest. Biologists will occasionally place rare falcon chicks with other more common falcon foster parents.

Biologists feed the newly hatched chicks with an adult peregrine puppet to avoid having the chick associate food with humans.

if the temperature rises more than a quarter of a degree over its preset value. The incubators also have little fans in them to help control the flow of air and the humidity.

Sandfort weighs one of his prized eggs. The eggs are supposed to lose 5 g — or 0.18 ounces — over thirty-one days. "This one should weigh 53.1 but it is four-tenths of a gram heavy. What we'll do is try to get it to lose that four-tenths over the next twenty-one days." Sandfort does some calculations on his computer to determine the proper humidity level the egg would need to shed its unwanted weight. "The computer says we should put it into a 30 percent humidity machine. But we have only 25 and 35 percent machines, so we'll put the egg in one machine for three days and then in the other for three days and keep switching until it hatches."

Not all problems during incubation are solved with such high-tech applications. If an eggshell is too thick, causing the egg to lose weight too slowly, even for the low-humidity incubators, Sandfort will merely sand the egg to reduce its thickness. Conversely, if it loses weight too rapidly he will often apply a coat of canning wax. And if an egg develops a crack, it may require emergency low-tech surgery — using Elmer's Glue.

Later that day Willard Heck, another of the center's falcon breeding specialists, enters the barn where the falcons are kept. Walking down a hall that traverses the individual chambers, he starts making falcon calls, "*eechip, eechip, eechip.*" One of the center's imprinted falcons now begins to return the call.

The bird is one of the center's nineteen imprints. Raised for their first three months around people and away from other falcons, these birds think they are human, and in fact consider other peregrines alien beings. Their purpose is to provide the center with semen with which to artificially inseminate the center's infertile egg layers. Heck enters the falcon's chamber. I stand before a one-way window and watch with amazement as the falcon excitedly greets Heck. To the falcon, Heck is his mate.

Even though the center has ninety pairs of falcons, only about half naturally mate with their partners. This does not stop the females from laying eggs, but the eggs — like a hen's without a rooster — are infertile. The center's biologists keep a close eye on the birds via the TV monitors to see which birds are indeed mating. If a pair is not mating, and the female begins laying eggs, they will artificially inseminate her.

Getting the semen for that process is Heck's job. From March through June, Heck will visit his peregrine mate daily, both bobbing heads to each other and making the appropriate calls, just as wild mates do. When the need arises to artificially inseminate a female, Heck will enter the chamber with a piece of quail meat and a special hat developed by biologist Lester Boyd.

Heck offers the quail meat to the falcon, who takes it and then returns it to the biologist, all accompanied with lots of bowing and piercing calls from both peregrine and man. With the falcon sufficiently aroused, Heck dons the hat. Then Heck turns his back to the male, as a female falcon would in the natural mating act, and the male mounts the hat and copulates with it. The semen, which catches in a special rubber dam on the hat, is then rushed to the infertile female.

After being reared in captivity, young falcons are placed in a hack box, like this one, from which they will learn to fly and hunt for themselves.

In the room adjoining the incubation chambers, in front of the TV monitors, the results of all these incredible procedures lie on soft towels in heated brooders, chirping for their dinner. A biologist feeds the young chicks "quail mush" — ground-up quail from the 120,000 Japanese coturnix quail the center raises each year.

During the height of the breeding season there can be as many as 120 chicks begging for their mush and hundreds of eggs in the incubators nearly ready to hatch. During that period it is not uncommon for biologists to work from five in the morning until ten at night.

After a few days the chicks will be moved out into the barns to be raised by foster parents — falcons who have already or not yet raised their own brood. Even the birds do double time to meet the center's goals. During the next thirty-two to thirty-five days, the chicks will balloon from about 1 ounce (28 g) to more than 20 ounces (560 g). They are then ready to be released in the wild.

HACKING

On a rocky bluff overlooking the blue Pacific at Point Reyes Seashore in northern California, I sit with biologists Jason Sutter and Laurin Jones at a hack site, staring through a spotting scope at two young falcons that are huddled against the cliff. Above the birds is the hack box in which they were placed when they were brought from the Predatory Bird Research Group. The group has its own peregrine breeding facility at the University of California at Santa Cruz.

It's the job of Sutter and Jones to baby-sit the birds, protect them from predators, and record their activity. Jason tells me he formerly worked at a hack site in Yosemite National Park in California, but he likes this site better. "The Yosemite birds didn't fly much at all. But these birds are much more active. I think it's the offshore winds; these guys love to fly."

The term "hack" derives from a falconry practice in which older nestling falcons were taken into the field where they finished feathering out and learned to fly while being fed on the top of a flatbed cart used by English cabbies or "hacks" to pull their fares. After flying and exercising for several weeks, just before they learned to hunt, they were captured back and trained for falconry.

The modern-day hack box is a special cage in which the birds are kept for about a week so they can get used to the site. Then the cage

Establishing peregrine nests in cities has made the peregrine falcon a media darling.

is opened and the birds are allowed to fly free, though they are fed thawed quail from the top of the box until they learn to hunt for themselves. Sutter and Jones stealthily place the quail on top of the box so the falcons don't associate the food with humans.

Although parent falcons do take part in training their young to hunt, biologists have found that young falcons can learn the process alone. Within six weeks, these birds will be catching their own food, and Sutter and Jones can go home.

The Predatory Bird Research Group has released 679 peregrine falcons in California, where now at least one or both members of half the nesting pairs in the wild were raised by the group. Centers like these across North America and Europe have been vital elements in the peregrine recovery effort.

A number of these birds have been released to major urban centers. Despite traffic and pollution, those falcons have done well, feeding on feral pigeon populations, which in the city are relatively pesticide-free. In fact, success ratios of urban and rural releases are almost identical, the advantage of pollution-free prey being offset by collisions with skyscraper windows.

Not all urban populations, however, are introduced. Peregrines historically have nested in European castles, bridges, windmills, and more recently on skyscrapers. According to Lloyd Kiff, director of the Western Foundation of Vertebrate Zoology, "it's not like we thought of putting peregrines in cities; they thought of it themselves. A big building is just another cliff to a peregrine."

Establishing peregrine nests in cities has also made the peregrine, as Kiff puts it, "a media darling," which has helped promote the bird's image as well as the recovery effort. Since 1977 peregrines have been introduced to a high building at the Tempelhof Airport in Berlin, to the cathedral at Cologne, and to several lighthouses on the North Sea coast.

In the United States, scientists have released captive-bred peregrines in Boston, Albany, Philadelphia, and Chicago. There are now five breeding pairs in Los Angeles and nine in New York City, including one on Wall Street. In Canada peregrines have been established at Edmonton, Calgary, Toronto, Winnipeg, Saskatoon, and Montreal.

A Lingering Problem

In general, populations of peregrines have increased in inland areas but are holding or even declining along coastal zones as rain slowly washes DDT residues down into the sea, and other contaminants, such as industrial chemicals, slowly move in currents along the coastlines.

And though DDT and dieldrin are no longer in use in most Western countries, even the newer, less harmful pesticides have been found to wreak their own havoc. Dr. David Bird, associate professor of ornithology at McGill University in Montreal, has been doing research on dicofol, a new pesticide used on citrus fruits and cotton crops under the brand name Kelthane. Dicofol has been found to cause embryo mortality and genetic deformities — it may even have the ability to change the sex of kestrel falcons. In Bird's captive colony of 350 kestrels at McGill, one male that was exposed to the pesticide grew both female and male sexual organs.

Dicofol is gradually joining DDT on the list of chemicals banned in North America and Europe. However, many unscrupulous chemical companies are dumping these toxic substances on Third World markets. In fact, DDT is still used in Africa and Latin America, though worldwide pressure may yet put an end to that.

As the peregrine recovers, scientists have begun to turn their attention to other species in Third World environments where rapid deforestation and habitat loss loom as the greatest menace to the falcons' future.

W.S. CLARK

Hobbies that breed throughout Europe
and Asia are highly migratory and
travel south to southern China, Burma,
the Indian subcontinent, and Africa.

Opposite:
The Australian kestrel, which breeds
in the open woods and parklands
of Australia and New Guinea, is
an opportunist. Responding to local
plagues of mice, it will then feed
almost exclusively on them.

The red-headed falcon hunts in pairs, one falcon chasing the prey and the other cutting it off at the pass.

PETER GINN

The lanner falcon launches low-level
attacks at birds near North African
watering holes — the falcon concealed by
its low approach until the last instant.

6
DRIVEN OUT OF
HOUSE AND HOME

Since Madagascar's independence in the early 1970s, the environment has rapidly deteriorated. So has the forest habitat of the Madagascar kestrel.

DAWN USHERS IN A CONCERT OF ANIMAL NOISES IN THE JUNGLES OF Tikal in Guatemala. Melodious blackbirds harmonize in flute-like melodies. Aztec parakeets, white-crowned and red lored parrots, and scarlet macaws play their own vocal instruments, while a lineated woodpecker pounds out the back beat on a jungle palm. The crescendo continues until daybreak, when the principal sopranos, the howler monkeys, join the cacophony, bursting out with lion-like voices that can be heard for miles.

I am sitting in the ruins of the Plaza Major. What was once the ceremonial gathering point of this 1,400-year-old Mayan city is now the centerpiece of Guatemala's largest jungle park. Tikal is to this small Central American country what Banff National Park is to Canada, or Yellowstone is to the United States. The protected wildlife within the park's boundaries is both plentiful and oblivious to human intruders.

On the jungle-covered trail that runs like a green tunnel up to the ruins, the spider monkeys rustle in the trees overhead as they crawl from limb to limb. At one point I stop for a troop of about fifty coatimundis, members of the raccoon family with banded snouts and tails, that are crossing the trail. In the morning the small gray foxes forage around the cabin as the oscillated turkeys spread their resplendent rainbow colors to the morning sun.

Tikal's five temples rise over the jungle canopy, giving a commanding view of the surrounding wildlife. The Plaza Major has two of these high pyramid-style temples at either end, with a number of smaller bleacher-like structures surrounding the ceremonial altars where Mayans sacrificed animals and humans.

J. DUNNING/VIREO

Bat falcons can be sighted over Guatemalan temples, deftly snapping up dragonflies in midair.

A view of Tikal's jungle from a temple ruin, on which bat falcons often perch.

Tikal has a number of falcons, including the barred forest falcon, the collared forest falcon, and the laughing falcon, but perhaps the most visible is the bat falcon. A pair of bat falcons nests at the south end of the plaza atop the Temple of the Jaguar.

The bat falcon is one of the smaller falcons. Males weigh an average of about 61 percent of the weight of the females, and are tremendously quick and agile hunters. Though the peregrine may be faster in the stoop or dive, the bat falcon, along with the merlin, the taita falcon, and the hobby, may be the fastest in direct flapping flight.

On top of the Temple of the Jaguar a male bat falcon is intently hunting: jerking his head up and down and from side to side, looking for prey to fly away from cover into a vulnerable position in the jungle air. Suddenly he spots something and dives off his perch. A few powerful beats of his wings and he is moving very swiftly, flying over my head, and leaving in his wake a loud *wooosh* that surprises and amazes me.

Bat falcons are dedicated aerial hunters that almost never hunt prey on the ground, preferring to take small birds, bats, and insects exclusively from the air. These falcons look regal with their dark wings, cap, and vest, chestnut pantaloons, and a whitish collar tinged with rust.

The bat falcon returns to the top of the temple, unsuccessful in his attempt, and continues the hunt. Suddenly his cry pierces the jungle as two large black vultures join him on top of the temple. He continues the commotion for a few minutes, but when the much larger carrion-eaters refuse to move, the bat falcon deserts his perch and flies to the top of a nearby tree stump.

The vultures are a serious problem at Tikal. The park used to have a nesting pair of orange-breasted falcons, a larger, rarer bird that looks much like a bat falcon. It was a matter of park pride, since fewer than ten nesting sites have been recorded in the world. However, the vultures chased the falcons from their nest. Park biologists feel the vultures are attracted to the garbage put out by the hotels and restaurants in the park. They've tried to encourage these facilities to be more sanitary with their rubbish, but the idea of ecology is new in Guatemala, even in Tikal.

The Not-So-Virgin Forest

Within the boundaries of the park the forest is thick and virgin — almost completely undisturbed. In populated areas just outside, the forest makes up only a quarter of the terrain, and very little of that is undisturbed. With clearcutting continuing at a rate of 3 percent per year, survey biologists predict that the total forested area could disappear within a decade.

Now the Guatemalan government, in cooperation with the United Nations' Man and Biosphere Program, has established the Maya Biosphere Reserve that will protect an area of 3.45 million acres (1.5 million ha) including Tikal and all the land north to the Mexican border. With Mexico and Belize creating adjoining biospheres in their own countries, the total area will be the largest contiguous protected area in all of Central America.

In many ways Guatemala is a microcosm of what is happening in other tropical Third World nations in Latin America, Africa, and southeast Asia. Virgin rainforest originally covered 4.2 million square miles (11 million km²) of the tropics, but now only 380,000 square miles (1 million km²) remain.

Disappearing habitat is a critical concern. Fifty percent of the animals on the planet live in the tropics, yet the tropics constitute only 10 percent of the landmass of the planet, and we know little of that area's raptor community. There are a number of tropical raptor species for which the first nest has yet to be found. As habitat dwindles, falcons come under increasing competition with other native species.

Tropical species don't share the same reprieve from DDT and dieldrin that their northern cousins do. Though the bat falcon is one of the most common falcons in all the lowland tropical forests of Mexico and Central and South America, it has become a rarity in the coastal Pacific farming communities of Guatemala. On the eastern coastal plains of Mexico north of Veracruz, biologists have been unable to locate any nesting bat falcons at historical nesting sites.

In both places nearly all the lowland forest has been cut for wood or to create agricultural fields. Eggshells of bat falcons in northeastern Mexico that were collected in the 1960s and 1970s showed 18 percent thinning, the same level that was so deadly to peregrine populations, and yet the use of DDT continues.

Within the boundaries of Tikal National Park, the forest is thick and almost completely undisturbed, but in the populated areas just outside, very little of it remains.

CO RENTMEESTER/THE IMAGE BANK

Tikal is located in the northern lowlands of Guatemala, in the province of Peten. Peten is typical of agriculturally developed tropical jungles. Though the jungle is a vital and rich biosystem, the soils beneath it are as good as sterile. "You scrape away the leaf litter," says Dave Whitacre, head of the Maya Project that is studying the raptor community in the Peten for the Peregrine Fund, "and you'll see there is a thin layer of leaf litter and essentially no humus. You get down to mineral soil almost immediately."

The leaf litter is rapidly decomposed by the incredible biomass of jungle insects. Leaf-cutter ants cut paths 6 or 7 inches (15 to 18 cm) through the leaf litter in Tikal. And the heavy rains leach nitrogen and potassium out of the soil. The nutrients in the tropics are essentially held within the trees — in the *life* — so when the forest is destroyed, the land is poor for agriculture.

SLASH AND BURN

On the road from the Flores airport in Peten to Tikal, we stop the car at a section of patchwork jungle that exposes the series of successions that typically occur with the slash-and-burn method of agriculture. In this method, farmers take a tract of forest and cut it down during the dry season. They let the wood dry for a month or so and then they torch it before the rainy season. Thus the nutrients in the trees are released in the form of ash. The farmer tills the soil and plants his crop just before the rains.

During the first season the crop is good, the insect pests and weeds are at a minimum, and the soil is rich, but with each successive crop, the soil gets poorer, the insects and the weeds build up, and the output grows weaker. In some areas farmers can get five to ten crop rotations, but in most areas after two or three rotations the field is abandoned and the farmer moves on to cut down another section of the jungle.

The slash-and-burn method is not all bad. After a field has been abandoned it begins to revert to its original state — what biologists call "primary forest." If farmers are doing rotation over a large enough area, it creates a mosaic of habitats in different successional states. It may maintain the maximum biodiversity of any agricultural system as long as there are large enough chunks of primary forest so that there are still apex predators like jaguars and forest falcons.

In the aboriginal system, when the human population densities are low, slash and burn is a fine agricultural method, but when the human population densities get too high, thereby increasing the demand for land and food, the forest is cut before it has a chance to mature. The soils grow increasingly infertile and the patches of immature forest that remain do not provide adequate habitat or food to maintain the abundance of animal life. Species disappear because they starve or they are unable to reproduce. "Ninety percent of the stuff that lives in the forest in Tikal," says Whitacre, gesturing to the patchwork jungle before us, "is not in these successional patches."

Biologists use the falcon as an indicator species. Just the presence of certain raptors is indicative of a healthy ecosystem. Protecting falcons at the top of the food chain means protecting all the species beneath them. In this way they function as an umbrella — if there are falcons, there will be healthy wildlife populations and healthy habitat as well. The falcon is thus a useful tool in the war to save the jungle.

Guatemala's environmental problems extend beyond its borders. On a two-hour walk through the jungle in Tikal, Whitacre and I spotted twenty-seven species of birds, twelve of them migrants from North America. The problems of pesticides and deforestation that Latin American birds face are shared by birds that come here only in the winter. Similarly, problems shared by Africa's birds are also shared by the migrants from Eurasia that migrate there during the northern winter, and the falcons that feed on these birds get a magnified dose of their troubles.

W.S. CLARK

Madagascar is the wintering ground for the sooty falcon, which feeds on the enormous insect population there.

To Madagascar

Madagascar shares many of the problems found in Guatemala. The island country is about the size of Texas, and lies 250 miles (400 km) off southeast Africa. It was once completely covered with forest, but now has 20 percent left, of which only 4 percent is undisturbed.

Since Madagascar's independence in the early 1970s, the environment has gone rapidly downhill. Silt run-off due to deforestation has begun to choke its rivers and rice paddies. Silt has even clogged the western port of Mahajanga, forcing ships to unload their cargo offshore. And silt is destroying the surrounding coral reefs, vital habitat for offshore marine life. But Western nations, including Germany, France, the United States, and Canada, as well as worldwide organizations such as the

World Wildlife Fund and the World Bank, have committed billions of dollars to rescue Madagascar's fragile ecosystem.

Madagascar separated from the continent of Africa 165 million years ago, when dinosaurs still ruled the world, so evolution there has taken its own direction. According to biologist Rick Watson of the World Center for Birds of Prey, "because of its isolation there are species found in Madagascar that exist nowhere else in the world."

Madagascar is the wintering ground for Eleonora's falcon and the sooty falcon. The sooty falcon is smaller than the Eleonora's falcon. Both species have uniform slate-gray backs and crowns, some of the same habits, and possibly a common ancestor, making them difficult to distinguish in the field.

Sooty falcons breed in the Middle Eastern desert and the offshore islands of the Red Sea, the Gulf of Aden, the Gulf of Oman, and the Arabian Sea. Sooty falcons and Eleonora's falcons feed on the enormous insect populations produced during the tropical rainy season in Madagascar, but the landscape is now vastly different from what it was once.

Madagascar's banded kestrel is perhaps the most affected by these differences, since it is a purely tropical-forest-dwelling species. We know little of the habits of this falcon. A nesting site of the banded

Mauritius, an island in the Indian Ocean, was once covered with tropical forest but now has less than 3 percent left.

kestrel was the last of all members of the genus *Falco* to be discovered. The nest was a basin-shaped depression in mossy plants on the upper branches of a large native tree.

Little is known about its feeding habits. The banded kestrel has been observed hunting chameleons high up on large trees, where it remains completely still until a chameleon makes a sudden move and reveals itself for the kestrel's attack. The banded kestrel is apparently adapted to hunting in dense foliage, unlike most kestrels, which hunt in open terrain. Its tail is longer and its wings shorter than other kestrels', giving it the ability to weave through the branches like a goshawk.

A French-English-American expedition to Madagascar in the early 1970s found the banded kestrel was rather common in forested areas of the northeastern part of the island, but forested areas are not as common today as they were then, and biologists want to take another look before it is too late.

The Most Endangered Falcon

At one point there were only nine Mauritius falcons in the wild, but through an intense international effort, their numbers have grown to more than 100.

In Mauritius, a country about 650 miles (1050 km) east of Madagascar, the problems are again repeated. Mauritius is an island of about 720 square miles (1840 km²) but with more than a million inhabitants, making it one of the most densely populated countries in the world.

Mauritius is famous for the dodo bird and about twenty other endemic birds, all of which have become extinct since the island was settled in the seventeenth century. Like Madagascar, Mauritius was once covered by tropical forest but now has fewer than 12,500 acres (5000 ha) of the original 425,000 (170 000 ha).

Those acres are of prime importance to the Mauritius kestrel, one of the rarest and most endangered falcons in the world. Mongooses, feral cats, and even monkeys prey on Mauritius kestrel eggs, nestlings, and the newly fledged young, which have a fatal habit of spending a lot of time on the ground in their first few days out of the nest. The bird hunts among the remaining forest canopy, feeding mainly on several species of geckos.

After a number of failed attempts to captively breed these birds, biologists have finally triumphed in a joint effort with the International Council for Bird Preservation, World Wildlife Fund, New York Zoological Society, Peregrine Fund, and Government of Mauritius. As a result of rescue procedures such as incubating the first clutch of eggs, guarding the nests from predators, and hack site releases, there are now twenty to twenty-five nesting pairs of Mauritius kestrels. The population has grown from nine individuals to more than a hundred in the wild.

Still, with the Mauritius kestrel remaining so reliant on the scant remaining forest stands, further progress had seemed impossible until biologists began hacking the birds in sugar-cane fields. These fields still have some remnant stands of trees along water causeways from which the kestrels can hunt. Since the kestrels were introduced to this area, they seem to have lost their reliance on the day geckos and are now eating a wide variety of birds and lizards found among the sugar cane. Encouraged by these results, scientists are toying with the idea of using foster parents of another bird-hunting species to train the young to go after birds. This would open up a larger portion of the food chain to the Mauritius kestrel.

The Taita Falcon

Some such inventive solutions may be necessary to preserve the taita falcon, which ranges in very sparse numbers in Ethiopia, Kenya, Zambia, and Zimbabwe. In coloration, size, and the shape of its foot, the taita falcon is much like the African hobby and in fact was thought

PETER GINN

Efforts to save the taita falcons in Zimbabwe have been hampered by revolution and war.

to be a hobby until recent captures and observations led scientists to believe that the taita falcon is, in fact, a miniature peregrine. It hunts more like a peregrine. The taita falcon catches most of its prey from a high, fast stoop, though it may dive below, come back up, and grab prey from beneath.

In the Zambezi Gorge below Victoria Falls in Zimbabwe, North American biologists and members of the Zimbabwe Falconers Club have been trying to census taita falcons, but have been hampered by land mines planted on the canyon rim during the last revolution.

The taita falcon is another one of the rarest falcons in the world, with an adult population that may number only a few hundred in the wild. The taita falcon in the Zambezi Gorge is threatened not only by mines but by Zimbabwe's plans to dam the gorge. The taita falcon must also contend with both DDT and dieldrin used in Zimbabwe to control mosquitoes and tsetse flies, carriers of malaria and sleeping sickness.

These pesticides affect not only the taita falcon but also migrant and resident peregrines. Since both species are bird-eaters, scientists are trying to determine if pesticides are having an effect on the taita falcon by taking a look at the eggshells of the now more common and less precarious peregrine.

THE FUTURE

On a tall Mayan temple in the jungle of Tikal, I sit with Miguel Angel Vasquez, a twenty-eight-year-old native Guatemalan, and stare out into the forest as the sun sets into the thick green jungle canopy. Miguel works as a park guard and part-time employee of the Maya Project, tracking radio-tagged falcons in the forest.

Suddenly Miguel points up at the silhouettes of two bat falcons approaching rapidly through the purple twilight. The pair begins circling the temple, no more than 30 feet (10 m) above us.

With a precision that defies description, they start hawking large tropical dragonflies out of the air, stooping down below their quarry and swooping up at the last moment, their legs and talons outstretched ... *whap!* ... a bat falcon plucks a dragonfly out of the sky, and ... *whap!* ... another does the same and ... *whap!* ... again. With binoculars I see them raise their dinner to their beaks and eat all but the legs, which fall away like scraps from a gluttonous feast.

We run around the high temple top anxiously, trying not to trip, both of us infected with the excitement generated by each successful attack.

In many ways the hope for the future of the falcon lies not so much with the birds in the air as with people like the young man now beside me. We of the industrialized nations, who have already cut our forests and destroyed much of our wildlife habitat, are now turning toward places like Guatemala, trying to enforce the message of conservation before their forest and habitat are gone.

But enforcement isn't the right way. In the end it will be the men and women like Miguel that we infuse with the excitement for wildlife and a better understanding of ecology who will take the message home to their people. This will ensure a future for the falcon. We can't do it ourselves. It has to be an inside job.

Unlike other birds of prey, which kill their victims with their sharp talons, the falcon merely holds its prey with its talons while it uses its notched beak to kill with a sharp bite that severs the spinal cord.

B. CHUDLEIGH/VIREO

The New Zealand hobby is more apt to use direct-flying or tail-chasing attacks on birds and thinks nothing of occasionally binding onto a rabbit or hare that may weigh six times more than itself.

Old World kestrels nesting in the Eurasian Arctic spend their winters in Africa, China, and the Middle East, though most of the kestrels in the United Kingdom stay there all year.

B. CHUDLEIGH/VIREO

W.S. CLARK

Lanners are large falcons that breed in the desert and dry savannah of southern Europe and Africa, where they feed mainly on birds.

JUAN M. RENJIFO/ANIMALS, ANIMALS

The aplomado is a striking, colorful Latin beauty that breeds in the tropical and desert scrub of Mexico and South America.

Opposite:
The rare taita falcon is found only in the wooded gorges and mountains of eastern Africa. It hunts small birds and insects from a full stoop in midair.

A young peregrine.

FALCON SPECIES

FALCONS ARE AMONG THE MANY ENDANGERED WILDLIFE THAT FACE DWINDLING habitat, pollution, and other threats to their survival. It is hoped that the following encapsulated information about different falcon species will help readers better appreciate the importance of these predators in the ecosystem. (For a list of birds of prey organizations that support falcon research and conservation, see page 134.)

This section gives information on common and Latin names, description, average weight, and distribution ranges. The order of the species follows the one given in the distributional and taxonomic list prepared by Dean Amadon and John Bull in *Proceedings of the Western Foundation of Vertebrate Zoology* (1988).

The Peale's peregrine is found along the North American west coast from Alaska to Washington, particularly around the Queen Charlotte Islands.

Common name:
Lesser kestrel

Latin name:
F. naumanni

Description:
Adult male has a chestnut crown and back with black markings, black outer wings, chestnut undersides, and a shiny white underwing. The adult female has a blue-gray crown, chestnut upper back, blue-gray lower back and tail, black outer wings, and pale buff undersides. The lesser kestrel is a small falcon that breeds in the steppe and forest-steppe of Eurasia and North Africa. Perhaps the most social of all falcons, it feeds in flocks, flying and hovering over the ground.

Average weight:
5.5 oz. (156 g)

Distribution:
North Africa, Eurasia

Common name:
American kestrel

Latin name:
F. sparverius

Description:
Adult males have a slate-colored crown with rusty patches, black mustaches, a rusty back with gray to black wings, and buff undersides with black spotting. The adult female is similarly patterned, but more generally rust-colored with a barred tail. A small falcon that breeds in the open lands and scattered woods of the New World, it preys mostly on insects on the ground, although it does take small birds, reptiles, mammals, and bats, some in the air.

Average weight:
3.5 oz. (100 g)

Distribution:
New World

Common name:
Old World kestrel
(Former name: common kestrel)

Latin name:
F. tinnunculus

Description:
Probably the most numerous falcon in the world. The adult male has a gray head and tail, a chestnut back spotted with black, and buff undersides. The adult female is more brownish and has a darker back with black spots on the back and undersides, and a thin mustache below the eye. A small falcon that breeds in the open lands and forest edges of Eurasia and Africa, it preys on insects, small mammals, small birds, and lizards, which it attacks on the ground, either from its perch or while hovering in the wind.

Average weight:
7 oz. (200 g)

Distribution:
Africa, Eurasia

Common name:
Madagascar kestrel

Latin name:
F. newtoni

Description:
Two color phases: adult male has gray-rust crown, streaked chestnut back, black outer wings, and whitish undersides. Adult female is similarly marked in this color phase, but with more chestnut in the crown. Also a dark phase where crown and nape are nearly black, dark chestnut back and upper wings, and dark streaked undersides. A small falcon that breeds in the open lands and forest edge of Madagascar and Aldabra, it preys mainly on insects, although it does take an occasional small mammal, reptile, or bird, mostly from the ground. Some insects are taken in midair.

Average weight:
4.5 oz. (128 g)

Distribution:
Madagascar, Aldabra

Common name:
Mauritius kestrel

Latin name:
F. punctatus

Description:
Crown and back are chestnut with black bars and streaks, while the undersides are whitish with large black spots. A small falcon that breeds in the native forests of Mauritius, it feeds mainly on lizards and small birds, which it takes on the ground or off the perch.

Average weight:
7 oz. (200 g)

Distribution:
Mauritius

Common name:
Seychelles kestrel

Latin name:
F. araea

Description:
Adult male crown is slate-gray with a dark chestnut back spotted with black, gray tail and wing tips, a faint mustache, and rust-buff undersides. The adult female is slightly paler. The smallest of falcons, it breeds in the forest clearings and palm trees of the Seychelles. It feeds mainly on lizards, which it snatches out of the trees.

Average weight:
3 oz. (85 g)

Distribution:
Seychelles

Common name:
Moluccan kestrel

Latin name:
F. moluccensis

Description:
The adult male is dark chestnut on back and crown with a gray tail and lighter chestnut undersides. The adult female is similarly colored, but has darker streaks and bars on her back, undersides, and tail. A small falcon that breeds in the open lands and forest edge of the East Indies, it preys on small mammals, lizards, small snakes, small birds, and large insects, mostly on the ground, although it can take insects and small birds from the air.

Average weight:
9 oz. (255 g)

Distribution:
East Indies

Common name:
Australian kestrel

Latin name:
F. cenchroides

Description:
Adult males have a pale gray crown and nape, pale chestnut back, a gray tail, whitish undersides, and dark gray outer wings. Adult females are a darker chestnut on head, back, and tail, with whitish, rust-colored undersides. A small falcon that breeds in the open woods and parklands of Australia and New Guinea, it preys on insects, small birds, and some rodents, which it takes on the ground while hunting from a perch or hovering in the wind.

Average weight:
6.5 oz. (185 g)

Distribution:
New Guinea, Australia

Common name:
White-eyed kestrel
(Former name: greater kestrel)

Latin name:
F. rupicoloides

Description:
The head, nape, and back are rust-colored with dark stripes and bars, dark outer wings, gray barred tail, and pale buff undersides. A medium-small falcon that breeds in the dry grasslands and scrub of Africa, it preys mainly on insects, although it also takes lizards, small mammals, and small snakes, mostly on the ground.

Average weight:
9 oz. (255 g)

Distribution:
Africa

Common name:
Fox kestrel

Latin name:
F. alopex

Description:
Reddish all over, paler underneath with black outer wings. A medium-size falcon that breeds in the semi-desert scrub and dry savannah of Africa, it preys on small mammals and large insects taken on the ground.

Average weight:
9.5 oz. (270 g)

Distribution:
Africa

Common name:
Gray kestrel

Latin name:
F. ardosiaceus

Description:
A slate-gray-colored bird with a paler throat and darker outer wings. A medium-small falcon that breeds in the savannah and tropical forest edge of Africa, it preys on insects, small reptiles, small mammals, and bats. Little is known about their hunting strategies, although they've been seen hovering over ground like other kestrels and catching large insects in the air.

Average weight:
8.5 oz. (241 g)

Distribution:
Africa

Common name:
Dickinson's kestrel

Latin name:
F. dickinsoni

Description:
Head and nape are whitish gray, back and wings are black, undersides are pale and brownish-gray, and the tail is pale gray with black bands. A medium-small falcon that breeds in the savannah and tropical forest edge of Africa, it preys mainly on insects and some small mammals and reptiles, but will chase small birds in flight.

Average weight:
8 oz. (227 g)

Distribution:
Africa

Common name:
Banded kestrel
(Former name: barred kestrel)

Latin name:
F. zoniventris

Description:
Head is gray with black streaks, dark gray back and tail, undersides are whitish with gray bars. Female is slightly darker than the male. A small falcon that breeds in the native tropical forest of Madagascar, it hunts chameleons in trees, although they've also been reported to take small reptiles, insects, and small birds on the ground and in cover.

Average weight:
7.5 oz. (213 g)

Distribution:
Madagascar

Common name:
Red-headed falcon

Latin name:
F. chicquera

Description:
Chestnut-colored head and facial stripes against white cheeks and throat, ash gray back and pale striped undersides. A small falcon that breeds in the savannahs and open woods of Africa and India, it is primarily a bird-eater. It hunts in pairs, one falcon chasing the prey and the other cutting it off ahead.

Average weight:
7.5 oz. (213 g)

Distribution:
Africa, India

Common name:
Western red-footed falcon

Latin name:
F. vespertinus

Description:
Adult male is dark gray, lighter on the undersides, with chestnut thighs and underbelly. Adult female is blue-gray, barred with black on back, while her undersides and head are orange. A small falcon that breeds in the open woods and forest-steppe of Eurasia, it preys almost exclusively on insects, which it takes on the ground or in the air.

Average weight:
5.5 oz. (156 g)

Distribution:
Eurasia

Common name:
Eastern red-footed falcon

Latin name:
F. amurensis

Description:
Both adult male and female are colored like the western red-footed falcon, only the small covert feathers, which cover the base of the quills on the underpart of the wing, are white. A small falcon that breeds in the forest edge and open woods of Asia. Little is known about its feeding habits on the breeding range, although it has been observed hunting insects on the ground and in the air at its wintering grounds in South Africa.

Average weight:
5 oz. (142 g)

Distribution:
Asia

Common name:
Eleonora's falcon

Latin name:
F. eleonorae

Description:
Most of the population is black on the crown and back with a whitish throat and reddish brown undersides. About 25 percent can be all black or smoky black, but patterned like the lighter bird. A medium-size falcon that breeds on the islands and seacoast of the Mediterranean, it preys on birds during breeding season by grouping up with other falcons and stooping or tail-chasing prey. In the nonbreeding season, it hunts insects out of the air.

Average weight:
13 oz. (370 g)

Distribution:
Mediterranean

Common name:
Sooty falcon

Latin name:
F. concolor

Description:
Slate-gray with dark streaks and darker outer wings, buff at the throat and a dark spot under the eye. Immature sooty falcons are browner with buff-edged feathers on the undersides. A medium-size falcon that breeds in the desert and islands of North Africa and Arabia. During the breeding season it hunts in pairs, preying mostly on migratory birds, taking them in the air. During the nonbreeding season, it hunts mostly insects, also out of the air.

Average weight:
11.5 oz. (327 g)

Distribution:
Arabia, North Africa

Common name:
Aplomado falcon

Latin name:
F. femoralis

Description:
Slate-gray back, rust-colored undersides, a gray bar across the chest, gray and rust-streaked crown. A medium-size falcon that breeds in the tropical and desert scrub in Mexico and South America, it preys on birds, small mammals, reptiles, and insects caught in the air or on the ground in direct attacks.

Average weight:
12 oz. (340 g)

Distribution:
South America, Mexico

Common name:
Merlin

Latin name:
F. columbarius

Description:
Male is slate-blue on back and crown, whitish throat and reddish-brown undersides with dark streaks and bars. Female is more uniformly brownish with white feather tips on the undersides. A small falcon that breeds in the open lands and forest edge of the holarctic, it preys mostly on small to medium-size birds, which it takes in the air as the bird flushes from the ground.

Average weight:
6.5 oz. (185 g)

Distribution:
Holarctic

Common name:
Bat falcon

Latin name:
F. rufigularis

Description:
It is a more common rendition of the rare orange-breasted falcon. It has similar coloring, with a lighter throat and brighter orange collar. It is a small falcon, half the size of the orange-breasted. It breeds in the tropical forests of the neotropics. It preys on birds, bats, and insects in swift, agile, aerial pursuits.

Average weight:
6 oz. (170 g)

Distribution:
Neotropics

Common name:
Northern hobby

Latin name:
F. subbuteo

Description:
Dark head and back, pale cream throat and cheeks, dark feathers underneath trimmed in buff with reddish brown thighs. A small falcon that breeds in the open woods and forest edge of Eurasia and North Africa, it preys mainly on flying insects and small birds, which it takes in the air with a repertoire of swoops, stoops, and direct assaults.

Average weight:
7.5 oz. (213 g)

Distribution:
Eurasia, North Africa

Common name:
African hobby

Latin name:
F. cuvierii

Description:
Dark gray back, crown, and mustache with rich red undersides. A small falcon that breeds in the savannah-forest edge throughout Africa, it preys primarily on insects, although it takes some small birds and bats close to the ground or at tree-top level in agile, aerial pursuits.

Average weight:
6.5 oz. (185 g)

Distribution:
Africa

Common name:
Oriental hobby

Latin name:
F. severus

Description:
Blackish head and back, whitish chin and throat, and dark brick-red undersides. A small falcon that breeds in the open forest of India and southeast Asia, it preys mostly on insects, although it takes small birds and bats in direct, high-speed, wheeling and flipping assaults in midair.

Average weight:
7 oz. (200 g)

Distribution:
Southeast Asia, India

Common name:
Australian hobby

Latin name:
F. longipennis

Description:
Black back and crown with a buff white and rust collar; upper breast is buff and lower breast is reddish brown with streaks. A medium-small falcon that breeds in the open forest of Australia, it feeds mainly on birds (some larger than itself) and some insects and bats, mostly from the air in a swift stoop.

Average weight:
9.5 oz. (270 g)

Distribution:
Australia

Common name:
New Zealand hobby

Latin name:
F. novaeseelandiae

Description:
Dark, blackish crown and back with undersides that vary from dark to pale buff with dark streaks. Throat is whitish with narrow brown streaks. A medium-size falcon that breeds in the grasslands and scrub of New Zealand, it preys on a wide range of birds and mammals, often by direct or tail-chasing assaults.

Average weight:
14 oz. (400 g)

Distribution:
New Zealand

Common name:
Brown falcon

Latin name:
F. berigora

Description:
Rust-brown head and back, dark brown tail and outer wings, streaked buff undersides, dark eyebrow and mustache. A medium-large falcon that breeds in the open lands and sparse woods of Australia and New Guinea, it feeds mostly on birds and small mammals. They will take mammals on the ground and will tail-chase birds even into dense cover.

Average weight:
20 oz. (567 g)

Distribution:
New Guinea, Australia

Common name:
Gray falcon

Latin name:
F. hypoleucos

Description:
Light gray back and crown with light speckled undersides and black outer wings. A medium-size falcon that breeds in the dry open woods of Australia, the gray falcon preys on small birds, mammals, and insects, which it takes in sudden surprise attacks at ground or shrub-top level.

Average weight:
15 oz. (425 g)

Distribution:
Australia

Common name:
Black falcon

Latin name:
F. subniger

Description:
Uniform sooty black to dark brown. A large falcon that breeds in the dry open woods of Australia, it feeds mostly on birds taken in the air, although it will take some prey from the ground. It attempts to intimidate its prey with loud screams.

Average weight:
24 oz. (680 g)

Distribution:
Australia

Common name:
Prairie falcon

Latin name:
F. mexicanus

Description:
Brownish back and crown, light cheeks streaked with darker brown, and creamy white undersides barred or streaked. A large falcon that breeds in the prairies and deserts of North America, it feeds on small mammals, reptiles, and ground-dwelling birds, which it takes in land-hugging, surprise attacks.

Average weight:
25 oz. (710 g)

Distribution:
North America

Common name:
Laggar falcon

Latin name:
F. jugger

Description:
Dark brown back, streaked reddish crown, pale yellow-brown or whitish undersides. A large falcon that breeds in the arid scrub and open forest of India, it preys mainly on birds, but takes small mammals, reptiles, and insects, hunting in a deadly tandem, one rustling the prey from the brush while the other attacks, or both alternately stooping at birds in the air.

Average weight:
17.5 oz. (500 g)

Distribution:
India

Common name:
Lanner falcon

Latin name:
F. biarmicus

Description:
Brown back with head and undersides that are generally sandy brown in North Africa. Lanners in Europe and South Africa feature a black forehead and mustache, bright rusty crown and neck, and creamy buff undersides. This large falcon, which breeds in the desert and dry savannah of southern Europe and Africa, feeds mainly on birds, although it also takes small mammals, reptiles, and insects. Hunts at or near the ground in low, ground-hugging, surprise attacks.

Average weight:
24 oz. (680 g)

Distribution:
Africa, southern Europe

Common name:
Saker falcon

Latin name:
F. cherrug

Description:
Brown back, with head and undersides that vary from pale cream with brown bars and streaks to a uniform brown. A large falcon that breeds in the steppe and forest-steppe of Eurasia, it feeds mainly on small mammals and some birds and lizards, which it takes at or near the ground in direct low-flying assaults.

Average weight:
35 oz. (990 g)

Distribution:
Eurasia

Common name:
Gyrfalcon

Latin name:
F. rusticolus

Description:
Ranges in color from white with dark streaks and bars to black with lighter spots and edging; most commonly an intermediate gray. The largest of the falcons, it breeds in the tundra and forest-tundra of the holarctic region. It preys on other birds (mostly the ptarmigan), but also some mammals like ground squirrels and Arctic hares, which it takes in ground-hugging attacks, chases, and occasional stoops.

Average weight:
50 oz. (1.5 kg)

Distribution:
Holarctic

Common name:
Peregrine falcon

Latin name:
F. peregrinus

Description:
Slate-gray cap and back, light barred undersides. A large falcon that breeds in open lands, seacoasts, and canyons all over the world, it preys almost exclusively on birds, which it takes in the air.

Average weight:
31.5 oz. (900 g)

Distribution:
Worldwide

Common name:
Barbary falcon

Latin name:
F. pelegrinoides

Description:
Also known as the red-naped shaheen, the barbary falcon is a close relative of the peregrine. Pale gray back, crown and nape a mixture of light gray and rust, pale undersides. A medium-large falcon that breeds in desert and arid scrub in North Africa and the Middle East, it preys on birds, which it takes in the air.

Average weight:
18 oz. (510 g)

Distribution:
Middle East, North Africa

Common name:
Orange-breasted falcon

Latin name:
F. deiroleucus

Description:
Black head, cheeks, and back; whitish throat with red crescent around the collar; orange undersides. A medium-size falcon that breeds in the tropical forest of the neotropics. A rare falcon and a powerful flyer, it feeds on birds, which it snatches out of the air with its huge talons over the forest canopy in direct aerial assaults.

Average weight:
16.5 oz. (468 g)

Distribution:
Neotropics

Common name:
Taita falcon

Latin name:
F. fasciinucha

Description:
Slate-gray crown and back, with whitish throat and cheeks, cinnamon undersides, and chestnut patch at back of head. A medium-small falcon that breeds in the wooded gorges and mountains of eastern Africa, it hunts small birds and some insects, which it takes in the air in full stoop.

Average weight:
9 oz. (255 g)

Distribution:
East Africa

BIRDS OF PREY ORGANIZATIONS AND RESEARCH GROUPS

The following people and organizations around the world either study falcons or work with falcon reintroduction efforts. Write for information or send donations to:

David M. Bird
MacDonald Raptor Research
    Center
McGill University
Ste.-Anne-de-Bellevue, Quebec
H9X 1C0 Canada

The Peregrine Fund, Inc.
World Center for Birds of Prey
5666 West Flying Hawk Lane
Boise, Idaho 83709
U.S.A.

Fonds d'Intervention pour
    les Rapaces
29 rue du Mont Valerien
92210 Saint Cloud
France

Peter Lindberg
Swedish Society for the
    Conservation of Nature
Department of Zoology
University of Göteborg
Box 25059
S-40031, Göteborg, Sweden

Padre Island Survey
3410 E. Columbia
Meridian, Idaho 83642
U.S.A.

Lynn W. Oliphant
Saskatchewan Cooperative
    Falcon Project
Department of Veterinary
    Anatomy
University of Saskatchewan
Saskatoon, Saskatchewan
S7N 0W0 Canada

Deutscher Falkenorden
Eickoffweg 25
2000 Hamburg 70
Germany

Predatory Bird Research Group
University of California
Santa Cruz, California 95064
U.S.A.

HawkWatch International
P.O. Box 35706
Albuquerque, New Mexico
87176-5706
U.S.A.

INDEX

Note: Page numbers in italics indicate illustrations.

accipiters, 7
aerial attacks, 51, 54
Afghans, 32
African hobby, 43, 110, 128
Akbar, 23–24
Al Nihayyan, Sheik Azyd bin Sultan, 36
Amadon, Dean and John Bull, 119
American kestrel, 49, 121; *43, 66*
ancient murrelet, 54, 65
Anderson, Bud, 69
aplomado falcon, 8, 43, 127; *116*
Approved Treatise of Hawks and Hawking, An, 26
Art of Falconry, The, 25
Art of Hunting, The, 24
artificial insemination, 92
Asia: history of falconry, 23–24, 33
Assateague, Island, Maryland, 66
Association nationale des fauconniers et
  autoursiers français, 37
"at hack," 27
Australia: peregrine population, 85
Australian hobby, 129; *19*
Australian kestrel, 123; *78, 97*

bald eagle, 84
banded kestrel, 108–09, 125
banding, 66–67, 74
barbary falcon, 10, 67, 132; *68, 79*
barred kestrel. *See* banded kestrel
Barnes, Dame Juliana, 31
bat falcon, 8–9, 13, 47, 103, 112, 127; *102*
beak, 7, 112
Beingolea, Oscar, 69
bells, 27
Bert, Edmund, 26
biomagnification of pesticides, 81
Bird, Dr. David, 95
Birds of North America, 28
Birds of Prey International, 38
black falcon, 9, 16, 130; *40*
black market, 38–39
blood samples, 74–75
Boke of Saint Albans, 30, 31
Booke of Faulconrie or Hawking, The, 26
boozer, 28
Boyd, Lester, 92
breeding, 47–50, 93
Britain, 25, 46, 63, 65; falconry, 25, 35, 37; *26*;
  peregrine population, 81–82, 85, 89
British Falconers' Club, 37
Brown falcon, 43, 129; *7*
brown pelican, 84

Cade, Tom, 8, 14, 16, 18, 39, 51, 85, 88

cadge, 28
Canadian Wildlife Service, 38, 87
Cape May, New Jersey, 66
captive breeding, 86–95
chicks, 50, 52, 54–56; *56–58, 62*; captive-breeding
  program, 87–88, hack box for, 93–94; hatched in
  incubators, 90–93
China: falconry, 33
Ciesielski, Marcus and Lothar, 38
clergy: falconry, 23
Cochran, Bill, 67–68
common kestrel. *See* Old World kestrel
conservation, 25, 39
copulation, 48, 92
courtship, 47–49
cross-fostering, 86, 93

d'Arcussia, Charles, 23, 35
De Arte Venandi cum Avibus, 25–26, 30
debonair, 28
DDT, 81–83, 95, 105, 111
defense of territory, 51–54
desert falcons, 9, 13
Deutscher Falkenorden, 37
Dickinson's kestrel, 124
dicofol, 95
dieldrin, 83, 95, 111
dive, 7, 12
DNA analysis, 74–75

eastern red-footed falcon, 65, 126
Edward I, 33
Edward III, 23
eggs, 49–50; *49*; effects of pesticides on peregrine,
  82–84; eggshell thinning, 83–86, 105; hatching
  in incubators, 90–93
Eilat, Israel, 67
Elizabeth I, 32
Eleonora's falcon, 16–17, 44–45, 47–48, 52, 53,
  55–56, 68, 108,126; *17, 48, 56, 69*
equipment for taming falcons, 27
Europe: ban on pesticides, 84–85; banding
  stations, 66; history of falconry, 23–35; nesting
  sites, 46; peregrine population, 83, 86, 89
European kestrels, 48
eyess, 28

Falconry in Two Books, 26
falconry: black market, 38–39; finding new birds,
  30; hacking, 93; history of, 23–26; language of,
  28; popularity faded, 35; purposes of, 30; royal
  hunt, 33–35; species of falcons used in, 32–33;
  status symbols in, 30; taming a falcon, 26–28;
  today, 36–37; *ii, iii, 23, 24, 26, 37, 39*

falcons: appearance, 7; beak, 112; captive-breeding
  programs, 86–93; chicks, 50, 52, 54–56;
  courtship, 47–49; defense of territory, 51–54;
  future of, 112; illegal trafficking, 38–39;
  migrations, 56, 63–76; nesting, 43–46;
  organizations and research groups, 134;
  predator, 18; prey, 14–18; size difference, 51;
  species, 8–10, 32–33, 119–33; speed, 7, 12–15;
  stoop, 12–13; talons, 15, 112; vision, 15;
  wings, 67
Falcons of the World, The, 51
female: artificial insemination, 92; eggs, 49–50; in
  falconry, 28; size advantage, 51
flying: chicks learn, 54–56; migration, 67–70
food: role in courtship, 47; size advantage of
  females, 51; taming falcons, 27
fox kestrel, 124
Fox, Nick, 8, 9
France: falconry, 37
Francis, Scott, 14
Frederick II, 25–26, 30
Fyfe, Richard, 63, 85, 87

Gentleman's Recreation, The, 26
Germany: falconry, 37; peregrine population, 83,
  86, 88, 89
Gilroy, Marty, 18
golden eagle, 31
gorge, 28
Göring, Hermann, 37
goshawk, 30–31
Goshute Mountains, Nevada, 1, 66
Grand Canyon, 2, 11
gray falcon, 9, 45, 130
gray kestrel, 124
greater kestrel. *See* white-eyed kestrel
Greenland Peregrine Falcon Survey, 54, 74
Guatemala, 101, 103–07

hacking, 27, 93–94
haggard, 28
Hall, G. Harper, 82
hawking. *See* falconry
HawkWatch International, 1
Heck, Willard, 92
Hickey, Joseph, 81
Hinde, Alan, *4–6*
hobbies, 8, 13, 31, 46, 65, 111, 128–129; *96*
Hoffman, Stephen, 1, 10; *4*
hood, 27
humans: banding falcons, 54; getting falcon
  used to, 27–28
Hundred Years' War, 23
hunting: male's skill, 47; parties, 33–35

illegal trafficking, 38–39
incubation, 90–93
International Conference on Falconry, 36
International Council for Bird
    Preservation, 110
Israeli Raptor Information Center, 67
Ivan IV (the Terrible), 33

jackdaws, 12–13
Japan: falconry, 24
Jarmen, Wally, 75
jess, 27, 36
Jones, Laurin, 93–94
Jura Mountains, 85, 86, 89

Kelthane, 95
kestrel, 8, 65, 95, 121–25
Kiff, Lloyd, 94–95
Kochert, Mike, 49, 52, 53
Kublai Khan, 33

laggar falcon, 9, 53, 131
lanner falcon, 9, 13, 30–32, 131; *99, 115*
Latham, Symon, 26
Leo X, 23
lesser kestrel, 47, 121; *20*
Lindberg, Peter, 86
Lombards, 25
Louis XIII, 23, 31, 35
lure, 27–28

Madagascar, 107–09
Madagascar kestrel, 122
Madison Peregrine Conference, 82
Maechtle, Tom, 73, 75
Magnus, Olaus, 32
Maktoum, Sheik Hamdan, 36
male: courtship, 47–48; defense of territory,
    51–52, 54; infidelity, 48–49
Mary I (Bloody Mary), 33
Mary Queen of Scots, 32
Mauritius kestrel, 110, 122
Maya Biosphere Reserve, 104
Maya Project, 106
McPartlin, Jeffrey, 38–39
Mediterranean. *See* Eleonora's falcon
Messouadene, François, 38
merlin, 8, 10, 13, 30–32, 46, 49, 65, 67, 127;
    8, 30, 57, 58, 65
mews, 28
Mexico: bat falcon, 105
Middle Ages: falconry, 23, 25, 30, 31
Middle East: falconry, 24, 36; illegal trafficking,
    38–39; migrating raptors, 66–67
migrations, 56, 63–70; Padre Island, 70–76
Mogador: Eleonora's falcon, 44– 45, 47–48
Moluccan kestrel, 123
Morizot, Don, 75

Nelson, Morley, 12
Nelson, Wayne, 13, 15, 47, 51, 54, 65
nesting, 43–46
New York Zoological Society, 110
New Zealand hobby, 8–9, 129; *114*
North America: falconry, 37; migrations, 65–66;
    peregrine population, 82–85, 87–88
North American Falconers Association, 37
North American Peregrine Survey, 85
northern hobby, 128

Oar, Connie, 75
Old World kestrel, 65, 121; *iv, 20, 114*
Oliphant, Lynn, 16
Operation Falcon, 38–39
orange-breasted falcon, 8, 104, 133
Oriental hobby, 128
osprey, 84

Padre Island, Texas, 2, 12, 53, 66, 68–76
Padre Island Peregrine Falcon Survey, 74–76
Palleroni, Alberto, 16, 70–75
Paximada: Eleonora's falcon, 44–45, 47–48, 53
Peale's peregrine, *120*
peregrine falcon, 8, 51, 54, 67, 132; appearance,
    10–11; courtship, 48; falconry, 30–32; migration,
    43, 69–76; nesting, 44, 46; population, 39,
    81–89, 94–95, 111; speed,12–14; *4–6, 10–15, 28,
    31, 49, 50, 59, 63, 66, 67, 70, 75, 81, 82, 84,
    87–89, 94*
Peregrine Fund, 12, 38, 87–89, 110
pesticides, 81–85, 89, 95, 105, 111
Philip the Bold, duke of Burgundy, 23
pitch, 28
Point Pelee, Ontario, 66
Point Reyes Seashore, California, 2, 13, 93
Polo, Marco, 32–33
prairie falcon, 9, 15, 46, 51, 64–65, 130;
    52, 59, 90
Predatory Bird Research Group, 93, 94
Presst, Ian, 82
prey, 14–18, 28, 51, 55; migrations for, 63–65
primary forest, 106
*Proceedings of the Western Foundation of Vertebrate
    Zoology,* 119
ptarmigan, 9

quail meat, 92–93
Queen Charlotte Islands, 44, 47, 50, 54, 65

radio transmitter, 36
rainforest. *See* tropical forest
raptors: establishment of Raptor Reseach
    Foundation, 86; in tropics, 105; migration
    studies, 66–67, 69
Ratcliffe, Derek, 81–84
red-headed falcon, 8, 125; *98*
Remple, Cheryl and David, 36

robin, 84
rock falcon, 31
Royal Falconry Establishment, 35
Rudradeva, Raja of Kumaon, 24

Saar, Christian, 86
St. Bavon, 25
saker falcon, 9, 14, 30–32, 39, 46, 131; *9*
Sandfort, Cal, 89–92
Scandinavia: peregrine population, 83, 86, 88, 89
Seychelles kestrel, 122
size, 51
slash-and-burn method of agriculture, 106–07
Snake River Birds of Prey Area, Idaho,
    2, 44, 52, 53
songbirds, 16–17
sooty falcon, 108, 126
sparrowhawk, 30–31
species of falcons, 8–10, 32–33, 119–33
speed, 12–15
stoop, 12–13
Sultan Beyazid, 23
Sutter, Jason, 93–94
swifts, 11

taita falcon, 13, 110–111, 133; *117*
talon, 15, 112; *16*
taming a falcon, 26–28
thermal updrafts on coastlines, 67
Third World, 95, 104
Thornton, Colonel, of Thornville Royal, 35
tiercel, 28
Tikal National Park, Guatemala, 101, 103–07
tropical forest: Guatemala, 101, 103–07;
    Madagascar, 107–09; Mauritius, 109–10
Turberville, George, 26

Ulysses, 25
U.S. Fish and Wildlife Service, 38–39, 74

Vasquez, Miguel Angel, 112
Veracruz, Mexico, 66, 105
vision, 15
vultures, 104

Wainwright Endangered Species Facility, 38
Walter, Hartmut, 45, 52, 68
Watson, Rick, 108
western red-footed falcon, 53, 125
Whitacre, Dave, 106, 107
white-eyed kestrel, 123; *61, 77*
William of Wykeham, 23
wings, 67
World Bank, 108
World Center for Birds of Prey, 89
World Wildlife Fund, 108, 110

Zambezi Gorge, 111